W9-CMS-317

ANTHOLOGY OF SLOVENIAN AMERICAN LITERATURE

with sixty reproductions of Slovenian ethnic art

Edited by
GILES EDWARD GOBETZ
Kent State University
and
ADELE DONCHENKO
University of Minnesota

Slovenski Ameriški Inštitut
Slovenian Research Center of America, Inc.

SLOVENIAN HERITAGE LITERATURE SERIES

29227 Eddy Road
Willoughby Hills, Ohio 44092 U.S.A.
Library of Congress Catalog Card Number: 77-77856

This book is gratefully dedicated to Slovenian American writers and poets whose love and works have enriched the Slovenian heritage and contributed to the richness and beauty of the American mosaic

Ivan Zorman (1889–1957), by Božidar Jakac

America, after all, is a composite whole of many nationalities that have been brought together by a common lot—that of seeking better opportunities, greater happiness. Each of these peoples has contributed something to American greatness. Americanism, therefore, does not mean the whitewash of uniqueness; it does not mean a mold from which all shall come looking alike, feeling alike, thinking alike. We may appropriately think of America as a mosaic made up of many stones and many colors blended into a rich harmony.

—Ivan Zorman, "Our Great Problem," in *Zarja*, the Official Organ of the Slovenian Women's Union, July, 1929.

Slovenian pioneers, by France Gorše

PREFACE

It is with mixed emotions of joy and trepidation that we present this very first anthology of Slovenian American literature. We are happy at the thought that this volume, long overdue, is now available to English-speaking readers. At the same time, we are painfully aware that no single volume can possibly do justice to the rich but still relatively unexplored area of Slovenian ethnic literature in the New World.

Writers included in this anthology are either immigrants from Slovenia or descendants of Slovenian immigrants. They have their historic and, frequently, their literary roots in Slovenia, the northernmost republic of Yugoslavia. Slovenia is a small, picturesque Alpine country which measures slightly less than eight thousand square miles—this is, approximately, half the size of Switzerland or about the size of Massachusetts.

Currently, somewhat over 1,800,000 Slovenians live in the Republic of Slovenia, in northernmost Yugoslavia. Yet, as pointed out by the English scholar R.G.A. De Bray, in his *Guide to the Slavonic Languages* (1951, p. 363), "all who know the Slovenes regret the fact that even after the 1914-18 war, this small people was far from entirely united within the frontiers of Yugoslavia." At the present time, there are still some fifty thousand to eighty thousand Slovenians under Austria, in Carinthia, once a completely Slovenian land which has been subjected to centuries of systematic Germanization and where the remaining Slovenians are currently struggling for their national and civic rights against the renewed and intensified genocidal fury of neo-Nazi elements. About 125,000 Slovenians remain under Italy and a small Slovenian minority survives in Hungary. The total number of Slovenian immigrants and their descendants on all continents of the world has been variously estimated between 600,000 and over a million, including some 500,000 Slovenian Americans in the United States. Thus, all Slovenians in the entire world number some two and a half million to three million souls.

A numerically small people located at one of the crossroads of Europe where Germanic, Italian, and Slavic nations have, throughout history, struggled for political and cultural supremacy, the Slovenians have endured and survived over a millenium of subjugation to incomparably stronger neighbors. Their very survival as a distinct Slovenian nationality group has never ceased to amaze foreign observers; it is, according to Bernard Newman, a British writer, "a miracle almost without parallel" (*Unknown Yugoslavia*, 1960, p. 199).

But the Slovenians *have* survived and, as the American author R.H. Markham put it, they "made their little country a model for Central Europe" and "moved forward to a distinguished place among the most advanced nations" (*Tito's Imperial Communism*, 1947, p. 11).

> Literacy in Slovenia reaches almost one hundred percent and the general level of urban, rural and domestic culture is high even by West European standards. . . . Slovenian is the language of one of the oldest documents written in any Slavic language, the Freising Leaves (Brižinski spomeniki), a manuscript written in Latin characters and containing prayers, confessions and homilies, believed to date from the eleventh century (R.G.A. De Bray, *Guide to the Slavonic Languages*, 1951, p. 363).

"The Slovenes used to share with the Scandinavians the reputation of being the best-read people in the world—the number of books read per head of the population was four times the British figure" (Bernard Newman, *Unknown Yugoslavia*, 1960, p. 198).

The Slovenians gave Sweden Carl Snoilsky, her great lyric poet, and France, Jean Vodaine (originally Kavčič), a poet, painter, and editor of *Dire*, which counted Hemingway and other literary immortals among its contributors. Have these Slovenians and their descendants also developed a Slovenian ethnic literature in America and, if so, what kind of literature?

The present anthology is the first systematic attempt to answer these questions. It offers the first comprehensive outline of Slovenian ethnic literature in America and the first cross-section of Slovenian American literature written in, or translated into, English. Twenty-three short works, all dealing with the Slovenian ethnic experience in the New World, have been included.

The book begins with selections grouped under the title "The Invisible Bridge." Americans, including Slovenian Americans, maintain more-or-less invisible bridges between their old and new countries and their respective cultures. Whatever names we may use for such bridges, to whatever degree we may or may not be aware of their existence, or whatever our attitudes toward them may be, these bridges exist, some visible and others invisible—built of our innermost thoughts, feelings, and longings. The Slovenian American writer, Louis Adamic, speaks very meaningfully of such bridges in one of his books, titled the *Two-Way Passage*. In this anthology, Kristan and others take us over such bridges.

Under the caption "Give Us Today Our Daily Bread," the authors present the work situations of Slovenians in the United States and, in one instance, in Canada. These descriptions are rooted in the personal experiences and observations of the writers and many of them are autobiographical. With the exception of Bukvich's "Sweeper Marich," where exaggeration and humor are used for literary effect, the descriptions are realistic portrayals of ethnic experience. This holds true even for Adamic's classic piece, "The Old Alien by the Kitchen Window," a true story of a Slovenian immigrant whose life in the factory is much more typical of that experience than is his unique retirement style.

"All Kinds of People" underscores the sometimes forgotten fact that members of an ethnic group are not "all alike"—that they differ in life styles, perceptions, and feelings, ranging from naive simplicity to avant-garde sophistication, from petty concerns to noble endeavors. With the exception of Zupan's "Cross-Spider," which is based on an old and long-abandoned superstition, all writings in this section deal with actual ethnic situations.

Finally, the ethnic American as a "marginal man" is dealt with in a literary manner under the title "A Soul Divided." It is common for recent ethnics to remain torn between two worlds and to be subjected to two or more sets of conflicting and incompatible inner longings and environmental expectations—an experience of the "marginal man" which is often just as painful psychologically and socially as it is stimulating and rewarding culturally, thanks to bicultural or multicultural exposure. If one accepts the thesis that an individual cannot fully understand his own culture without knowing at least one other culture, then the concept of marginality—of souls divided—should be a very rewarding one to ponder.

The editors have endeavored to present, as far as possible, a fair and unified cross-section of Slovenian ethnic literature in America, centered on themes of ethnic experience in the New World. Although some of the writers included in this anthology have long enjoyed national and, occasionally, international recognition, some selections have been included not because of their clearly demonstrated literary excellence but in order to illustrate various levels, concerns, and styles of Slovenian American literature. Twenty of the twenty-three selections come from Slovenian American writers in the United States and three are by Slovenian Canadian immigrant authors (Daniela and Ivan Dolenc and Ted Kramolc).

The senior editor was responsible for the review of Slovenian American literature (Part V), for choosing the selections for this anthology, and for securing the cooperation of the authors, translators, and publishers. The junior editor has polished and, in many instances, rewritten the translations and has transformed the uneven materials into what we hope is now a reasonably unified and worthwhile volume.

We are deeply grateful to the publishers of copyrighted materials for their permission for reprinting, to all translators and artists for their fine cooperation, to all benefactors and friends for faithful support and encouragement; to our spouses, Milena Gobetz and Fedor Donchenko, for their inexhaustible patience and loving help; and to Mrs. Patrick Cleaver for valuable advice, expert typing, and technical assistance. Our deepest gratitude, however, goes to all writers, living and dead, whose contributions make up this volume. Should the present anthology help, even a little, to promote an interest in and appreciation for Slovenian literature and heritage, should it enrich the American mosaic with a few colorful pebbles, then we will feel amply rewarded for our efforts.

Giles Edward Gobetz
Adele Donchenko

CONTENTS

IV
A SOUL DIVIDED

V
SLOVENIAN AMERICAN LITERATURE

ART WORKS

I

THE INVISIBLE BRIDGE

Etbin Kristan (1867–1953)

Etbin Kristan

THE INVISIBLE BRIDGE

Translated by Rick Sustaric

An enormous, giant-like, black bat hovered over the land, casting shadows into every valley and winding the peaks with an ominous darkness. It really was not a bat; the people did not know the right name for it. A terrible nightmare pressed on breasts and sapped the living air out of lungs. A pent-up feeling flamed in the heart, but it could not burst out; it could not be expressed. The mind gave birth to a thought, but it could not see the light of day; it could not be uttered.

"We live on our land; this is our ancestral soil; here we were born, we and our parents and their parents; here are rooted our rights," spoke the people.

A harsh, roaring voice thundered a reply: "Laws are written by the lord and ruler of the land and he alone deals out justice. What he decides is right and the servant and serf do not judge about rights. You were bondmen, slaves; too quickly have you forgotten the whip and the white-hot crown."*

A quiet, barely audible thought murmured a whisper: "We are people as you are; we plow and sow; you, however, reap and enjoy. Who should be thankful? Who should endure?" It did not dare express itself aloud because the thought was insurrectionary, seditious, revolutionary and, as such, first among mortal sins.

The law declared: "Bow, submit to the lord!"—and bow they did, even though they were exhausted with oppressive, backbreaking labor. Furthermore, declared the law: "Give to the lord the share which he demands!" and give they did as commanded, even the portions from their own mouths and from their own needs.

---

*"White hot crown" refers to Matiya Gubec, who in 1573 led a peasant uprising in Slovenia and parts of Croatia. He was defeated and put to death by being crowned with a white-hot iron crown.

SOURCE: Etbin Kristan, *Povesti in črtice* (Chicago: Prosvetna Matica, 1945), 79-90.

The eye of a storm, by John A. Kapel

When there was a holiday, they broke into song that they might forget their cares and troubles, their torment and anger. But a voice bellowed: "Stop! Cease with such singing. It is forbidden. Sing songs of submission and respect as befits bondmen."

They unfurled their own banner on that festive occasion, but an order cried out: "Not here! Hoist up the lord's standard, that it may flutter and wave over the roofs and steeples, over the mountain tops and over the whole land."

Rules and regulations, laws and prohibitions, constables and courts, the lord's officialdom and red tape and damp jails —life was a narrow path, circumscribed on every side, and you did not dare close your eyes or absent-mindedly stumble onto notions or thoughts lest your foot overstep onto forbidden ground set with snares and traps. Everything was rigidly structured, strict law and order prevailed, but there were some who, at night when utter silence reigned, in the innermost depths of their soul thought that order choked life and that law had slain justice.

There were restless spirits who did not know how to submit and who lived from day to day hoping, believing in the morrow, and telling others that it was necessary to prepare for that future. If they dared to speak, their mouths were muzzled and their hands chained. All the days and all the years and all the centuries must be, and must remain, as the lord dictated, for even one silent notion for change was perverse and criminal.

The restless spirits, however, fled across the borders of the country, across the widest ocean to the very distant unknown places, where they expected, anticipated, and awaited a different justice and broader paths of opportunity. The more rigid and ironclad the lord's law and order became at home, the more inviting became the fabulous places of strange and foreign lands.

"You, too, Toné?" asked Yuri in a voice of surprise and amazement.

"Yes, even I, dear friend," replied Toné, and it was obvious it was not an easy decision for him. "If I cannot breathe the life-giving air of freedom, I will perish. I feel choked that I cannot breathe. Oppressive cramps and spasms crush and numb my bones and organs and my head reels from the heavy aches of prohibitions and forbidden thoughts. Something, some force, is drawing me away before I am utterly poisoned by this oppressive and contaminated air."

"Endure! Submit as we do!"

"I cannot submit. If I stay I will break thousands upon thousands of rules and laws and run up against a million prohibitions. I am not afraid of imprisonment. I have experienced jails. The whole land is one grand slave pen, one huge prisoner's quarry. Law officers, tax collectors, officials of all kinds have you in their grip before the courts and other high places. Constables eye every path you take—to your home, to the fields, to the woods, and even to your bedside. Fear has no power over me. What bothers me is that life is so empty, work has no meaning or sense, and so much is wasted and lost."

"If you leave, you yourself will be lost. Strange and foreign lands will swallow you up. You will speak a foreign language, sing foreign songs, fall in love with foreign people and in the end forget your homeland."

Toné answered with a negative nod. "I am leaving because I cannot and will not forget. I must go away if I am to preserve whatever spark of love is still within me. My soul and all my deepest feelings depart with me."

Yuri could not understand. His head rocked from left to right. He looked at his friend, held and pressed his hand with poignant pain. Then he turned, lifted up his arms, and walked away. "One more lost son who forsakes his mother. . . ."

Great and expansive is the foreign land and also very strange. For a long time the many Tonés, Johnnies, and Yerneys did not understand it—some never understood it. From some, the foreign land just took and took, and even reproached them for the crust of bread for which they gave their sweat, their health, and even their very life. To some this strange land gave nothing, to others a morsel, and to some a great deal. In a way it was just as in the homeland. The goddess of fortune is the same and life is a gamble, a game as at home. You lose, you win—and then some will say, "He is shiftless, worthless," or they might say, "He is a magnate." Take Pepché, who bought some worthless papers from a man who wanted to be rid of them; suddenly everything changed—Pepché did not know how or why. Today he rides in a limousine, he has a palace, and people bow to him. It doesn't bother or faze him at all that he forgot his mother tongue and learned a new one. Martin worked twelve years in a mine. Then there was an accident, a cave-in. He rescued the lives of three comrades. He himself perished and is buried in a pauper's grave.

Whoever left the homeland without a soul did not find one overseas; whoever left the homeland with his soul did not lose it abroad.

Between the old country and the new one, however, there are deep valleys, high mountains, wide rivers, and an even wider and more distant ocean. A hand cannot reach across such a great expanse and a word is lost even before it is uttered. Life has many paths; one leads here, others lead elsewhere in many directions. How could we know what they were doing in the distant foreign land, when one cannot see that far or hear from such a great distance?

Once a whole group of emigrant Johnnies returned to the homeland. On their coats and jackets they pinned symbols and momentos of foreign places—symbols which declared the fact they belonged together. The people at home looked and said: "Did you notice? Publicly they declare that they have become foreigners. They are no longer ours."

Back in the homeland, they began to build a big house, preparing for the festive day when it would be finished. They sent letters to the foreign land stating what they planned to do and enumerating how many bricks, stones, and how much lumber and glass would be needed and how the entire interior would be furnished and decorated. In the foreign land, however, there were hard times. Something strange happened. Thousands of Johnnies and Peters from Slovenia with millions of Williams, Patricks, and Vaclavs began to knock on doors which did not open. They counted their last coins which began to vanish as fast as a desert puddle. There was barely enough for bread, without butter—for today and maybe some for tomorrow, and then what?

Back in the old country, it was not possible to conjure up enough silver or paper notes for the big house, for the turrets and painted windows. So they pondered and concluded: "We knew all along that they would forget us. Selfishness overcame them in the foreign land. The greedy doctrine of each for himself rules them. They are as lost to us as if they had drowned."

* * *

Violent and terrible storms blew over the earth and did not spare the homeland. Thunder crackled, lightning pealed across the skies, the earth shook and graves swallowed up entire legions. Death became so common that it no longer stirred a soul or pierced a heart. Violence put off its mask, boldly and loudly declaring that it alone was the source of right. Blood soaked the land, enormous pieces of steel fresh from the furnaces ripped, raped, tore, and crushed the earth with deep holes. The explosions, cries, and laments, propelled by a bloodthirsty drunkenness, boiled into more hatred, more hostilities. However, during rare hours of sobriety enemies exchanged tobacco for bread, cigarette lighters for cheese and jokes for jokes. When the trumpet sounded the alarm, they were again at each other's throats—killing. There were moments when they all asked: "Why?" They received no answer. They were not able to ask those who did know. . . .

In the faraway foreign land hearts also bled with sorrow, but in the homeland they did not know this. A handful of local Johnnies could not stop the madness which the powerful on thrones could no longer restrain. Yet, in time, this madness, too, will end just as floods, drought, and earthquakes subside. What will happen to the homeland then? Rays of sunshine filter through even the thickest darkness and goodness springs forth from even the most terrible horror. So immigrants strained to tell the world about their poor native land—its trials, sufferings, hopes, and rights.

Wailing in the wilderness, by France Gorše

But between the homeland and the foreign land there were hills, rivers, and the boundless ocean.

The beasts of war were finally overpowered. They buried the dead and hid the blind and disabled as best they could. They signed many papers and documents, rearranged many boundaries like farmers shifting fences and fence lines. A new life began. They wiped their tears away and one could hear the cries of happiness and the songs of fulfillment.

In the faraway land across the sea they nodded in assent; their eyes gleamed with approval. There was much suffering and many were buried in the dark earth and would never return. But the sun appeared to shine brighter with promises for a better future. Satisfaction eased their new tasks and lightened their endeavors and exertions.

Hopes are most beautiful when the dawn glows with bright promises across the sky after a long night. Yet, time devours minutes and hours and pales the dawn's colorful glow; many a bright expectation receives a sudden slap. Beautiful were the beginnings; beautiful was the dawn in the homeland. Yet, like youth in the month of May and virginity, beauty is fleeting. The homeland is not an island upon which shining gods and good nymphs would establish a paradise, safe from the cruel encroaching hands of the world. Tempests and thunder may cease, but when the wineskins are filled, sudden storms burst out, raining fear and destruction. Water freezes and water evaporates into stifling heat; it gathers in rivers and in clouds, and thunderstorms again shake the air. Threatening furies soar over the north and south and spread fear and horror over the homeland.

Oh thoughts, so beautiful, so high and free, do you again hear prohibitions? Oh yearnings, so gentle and noble, so warm and passionate, is the heart again bound with fetters? Oh you restless spirits who seek fulfillment, who yearn for truth, for rights, who soar upwards toward the sun to kindle torches—did the old order again return, the order which commands the serf and restrains the oppressed with prohibitions, binds the eyes, muffles the ears, and clips the wings of freedom? Did the years circle full around and return back to those times we believed were long since gone and buried? . . .

Yuri walks long, lonely paths because he fears his thoughts yet cannot live without them. People have become silent and mute; words are dangerous whether they be expressed or not. You feel or think that you denied or repressed your thought, but a listener or an eavesdropper deciphered it, perhaps because it also crossed his mind. How can one know how a neighbor, once a close friend, will judge your thoughts when his daily bread is more important to him than friendship.

Yuri's thoughts are alive, very powerful. More than half of his life is in his thoughts. If you want to destroy his thoughts, you will have to kill him, too.

It is not enough that thoughts linger in his head. They seek the light of day. They must get out or his skull will burst. But they are forbidden and they must not even come to the tip of his tongue. What would it profit or avail if he went to the top of a mountain and there bravely screamed out his thoughts into the valley? At that moment his hands would be fettered, his mouth muzzled, and his thoughts would linger in darkness. But they must come out, they must see the light of day, they must be in the world—they must or they will choke him; they must be shared because they are true and just. They must be uttered because they were begotten by life itself; they must be heard; they must meet thoughts from other minds and hearts, equally begotten, and united with them, to grow, to become a powerful beacon, the flaming *Shekinah*, which led the oppressed tribes to the Promised Land.

Who will utter the word, express the thought labeled dangerous which must not be spoken? Who? . . .

Day after day along the scenic paths Yuri walks alone with thoughts as his only companion. Far from the town he walks, past the meadows, through the woods, to where no spy hides, where the forest murmurs and sounds accompany his thoughts as the keys of a piano accompany one another. Today he climbed to the very top of the hill. . . .

Who should speak? Who should utter the word, as vital as bread and water, which lingers on his tongue all the day long but cannot be expressed? To whom may he unburden himself? In whom should he trust? How and from where may the thoughts break out into the light of day? . . .

Listen!

What delusion or trickery, troubling and confusing, hides in the evening air? Are his nerves so highly strung that either madness or death is near? Did the word become such a mania that he hears the ineffable thoughts as if they came from the heavens, or from some bottomless pit, or from the other side of the world? Yet, it is all in his head, in his soul, like an untamed lion, and silent as the grave.

No! Yuri, it is not madness; it is not a mad fantasy. If you strike on one string, all related strings respond in kind. The world is vast and encompassing, but thought is powerful and laughs at great distances. The strings of your soul were struck and found an echo in another, like yours, which yearns, strives, hopes, and believes as yours does. It receives your word which came to it across an invisible bridge, past the hills and valleys, across the distant ocean. It meets, catches, and utters your word so that it is heard, that it resounds throughout the world until it is fully realized.

"I am leaving because I want to preserve love; my soul and all that is within me departs with me," declared Toné when he left. And behold his soul is alive and all that is within him remains as before. The same strings are tuned in him so that his spirit responds to the strings of great joy or deep sorrow in the homeland. He must live in a foreign country; his feet must tread foreign ground; his hands must dig foreign soil, turn foreign wheels, lift foreign burdens, count foreign numbers, build foreign homes, and raise foreign children. He kneads his bread from the wheat of foreign fields and covers his nakedness with the cloth of foreign weaving. His labor has been appropriated by the foreign land and there he builds his future. How could Yuri despise him for he breathes his air and drinks his water, and through him and in him he has found people, sensitive and thoughtful, suffering and fearful, yearning and hopeful, similar to him, his comrades, his co-workers and co-warriors?

The homeland still lives in Toné's soul. When joy reigns at home his soul is also uplifted, and when misfortune strikes his soul feels all the grief and pain. In the hours of greatest suffering a silent word, a thought, suffices, and another soul understands, accepts, and fulfills its desire.

This forgotten son of the homeland is far away, changed; some customs and ways he gave up and took on new ones; he shaves daily and his chin is always smooth; he speaks a foreign tongue, but he is not lost. From heart to heart, from soul to soul, for joy and sorrow, for suffering and striving, for wishes and hopes and for an inexorable faith in the future, there is an invisible bridge. No earthquake can shake it, no bomb can destroy it, for undying love walks across that bridge with inaudible steps.

Daniela Dolenc

Daniela Dolenc

SURVIVORS

The scorching sun beat against the well-guarded prison windows which were covered with black paper. In Cell 104 the female prisoners were awakening. They stretched their tired limbs and stared silently into the outline of the sun's rays that filtered around the edges of the paper. Each busied herself with her own burden.

I was the youngest among them. I was only fifteen. Lying beside me was a middle-aged woman, the mother of two. She got up from her spot on the floor and began catching lice in the uncombed hair which hung limply about her shoulders. She caught them one after another mechanically, turning from time to time to kill a few fleas which happily jumped over the straw mattress.

"How long will all this last?" she asked harshly. "I can't stand it very much longer; I itch all over. And how are you today, my child?"

"As on any other day," I replied. "I'm hungry, I itch and, worst of all, the pain in my legs bothers me more and more." The vitamin deficiency had opened the wounds on my legs and pus spattered from them onto the straw in a regular stream.

"If we only had a bandage," Mrs. P. said to me. "I already gave you all my underwear—there is nothing left."

"It will go away somehow," I comforted her. She worried over me constantly as though I were one of her children. They had been taken from her when she was arrested and she had no idea where they were. She did not talk about them often but at night she sobbed painfully and in her dreams she called out their names.

Gradually all the women prisoners began to kill the vermin plaguing them. We did this daily in place of a morning wash. Each day the Gestapo woman Tuschka placed one pitcher of water in the cell; this had to serve forty-eight prisoners. There was not enough water for our thirst, much less for washing.

SOURCE: *Veterans Review*, Remembrance Day Issue, 1974, 3-11.

A strong stench came from the corner where the toilet pot stood. I desperately needed to urinate but the pot was already too full to accept any more. God forbid that the contents overflow before Tuschka arrived! Again a prisoner would be beaten and sent to the bunker for three days.

We started our usual game of guessing the time. The sun was already high—that meant breakfast was near. A jingle was heard at the door and the hated traitor-renegade stood there with her company, two Gestapo guards. We jumped to attention and into line. The prisoner nearest the door reported, "Cell 104, forty-eight women."

Recently Tuschka had been speaking in a lower tone. Today she did not even look into the pot in the corner but merely signaled two prisoners to carry it away, which they did, accompanied by a Gestapo guard on either side. The rest of us greeted her with an empty gaze. She poured some black water into each of our military mess tins and left one small loaf of bread for all of us.

We hurriedly gulped the coffee and swallowed the entire portion of bread which was the ration for the whole day.

The city of Maribor is located in northeastern Yugoslavia near the Austrian border. The British and Americans often bombed the city which was a production site for German weaponry and ammunition. The approach of the bombers made the citizens of Maribor happy rather than frightening them. They were eager for the war and Nazi terror to be over as soon as possible. Ever since my imprisonment behind the thick jail walls, my heart beat wildly at the sound of the siren. Together with the other prison inmates I prayed that no bombs would fall on us.

During the year and a half I had been imprisoned, we had had no news of what was happening outside the prison walls. We did know that April of 1945 had arrived and that the next day was Easter Sunday.

I thought of all the goodies my mother had so carefully prepared for us children for this holiday. We were not wealthy. There were eight children at home, all healthy and strong. My father had been an army officer but he was already on pension when the Germans invaded. They scattered all of us; my father and mother were separated at a railroad station and sent to different concentration camps. I thought of my people and wondered if they were still alive. I clung to Mrs. P. as a symbol of my parents, my brothers, my sisters, my home, and I confided only in her. On numerous occasions she had given me her ration of bread and I will never forget how she took my part against the other women in the cell.

Suddenly I wanted to see myself in a mirror. I had not looked in a mirror for a whole year and a half. What did I look like? In spite of the horrors of prison life I wanted to be beautiful, to be admired. I asked for a mirror. The prisoners around me screamed in one voice, "A mirror—in these times! What does she think, anyway? She should thank God just to be alive!"

Mrs. P., with tears in her eyes, intervened, "How inconsiderate of you! Don't you see that she is developing from a child into a young woman? Nature doesn't wait because of the war. If any of you is lucky enough to have a mirror hidden under your prison uniform, give it to her. If you don't, I shall have to. . . ."

All confessed that they had no mirror. Suddenly they became quiet; perhaps they felt guilty.

Noon was approaching when the siren sounded. Alarm! We clasped our hands—our allies were coming again! The thunder began and the explosions came closer and closer to the prison walls. Suddenly, the cell was filled with a thick darkness and dust swirled on all sides. Shrapnel whistled and human screams and prayers mingled with the thunder.

I crawled along the floor toward the door which was always closed and reached for the handle. Just then the door was gone and a huge hole was in its place. "Forward, forward," I kept encouraging myself as I rose and stumbled into the dark corridor. Screams and confusion continued behind me. "Maybe, maybe I can manage to escape," shot through my brain, "to be free."

Three guards with machine guns stood at the end of the hall. "Into the cellar!" they shouted. The thunder had subsided and together with the other female prisoners I dragged myself toward the cellar. The male prisoners, from whom we had been strictly separated, now joined us. The cellar was a mass of bodies. As many as could had wrapped themselves around the strong pillars of the prison foundation. The darkness was so thick that I had to grope to find an empty spot for myself. The explosions returned and everywhere I heard cries of "God help us!" I dropped to the floor and felt another body close by.

"Who are you?" I asked.

"No questions!" was the answer out of the darkness. "It doesn't matter who I am. I am just another prisoner like you. Here, I have a blanket. Wrap yourself in it; you're shaking all over."

"How old are you?" I persisted.

"Seventeen—and you?"

"Fifteen."

"You are even younger than I."

"What do you think is going to happen to us?"

"They say that the war will be over soon. It has to end, if only because we have a whole life ahead of us," he said. "Of course, that's if we stay alive. And if we don't, who cares? I'm fed up with everything anyway. I feel like I'm a hundred years old. And you?"

"The same. I've read so much about youth—what youth?"

Survivors, by John A. Kapel

"You and I never knew it. From childhood straight into the dying age—that's what we know." His voice was sad. I told him how sorry I was that he could not see me. I also told him what Prisoner P. had said: that I was a young girl, and if it were not for the lice and fleas I would be very pretty. . . .

"I shall see you if we ever get out of this hole alive. And then you must take a good look at me—maybe I, too, am still young and maybe good-looking."

Somehow, the explosion of the bombs and the moaning of those injured by shrapnel was easier to endure. Somehow, it was not so important that the bombing stop immediately.

But it did stop shortly. Again we heard the siren, this time announcing the end of the air raid. The Gestapo personnel began to shout and use their fists as they rushed us to the stairway. We were halted on the second floor and someone announced that the cells on the floor above were without doors —the air pressure had ripped them off their hinges. We would all have to be housed on this floor.

They began to separate us into groups. Later, after the war, I learned that many of my co-prisoners were shot on that day. Room had to be made only for those of us who remained.

Now I could see my good compatriot clearly: he had blue eyes, curly hair, and, yes, he was young and handsome. His smile was bitter as we parted hands and I waved goodbye to him. A guard pushed him to the side where the male prisoners were assembling. What did he think of me now that he had seen me for the first time? Was I attractive? I could not know the answer.

So many prisoners were crowded into our cell that there was no room to sit down. Lunch—that so-called soup with corn-meal—did not arrive and we were told that there would be no supper either—not even the usual thin liquid with two potato peels floating on the surface.

I was completely exhausted. I looked for Mrs. P. but I could not find her, nor had any of the others seen her. The fear and sadness came over me, like never before in the prison. I felt an urge to scream aloud, but suddenly I trembled all over. What is going to happen now? What are they going to do with us?

That night I hardly slept. Early in the morning I was awakened by the turning of the key in the door. It wasn't the female devil. There stood a Gestapo decorated with many medals. He called out names from a list. My name was called and I stepped out into the corridor where a number of girls about my age were already standing. The gloomy guard shouted an order: we were to wait here.

From around the corner came a whisper—it was my friend from the cellar. He hurriedly transferred a cookie from his hand into mine. He said that he had stolen it from the Gestapo wife whose apartment he cleaned. I could not accept this

United in suffering, by Lillian Brulc

treasure. "No, keep it yourself; you are hungry," I protested. But my friend was already at the other end of the corridor. The Gestapo shouted at the male prisoners that they were not to communicate with us. I clutched the cookie in trembling fingers while huge tears rolled down my cheeks. Wrapped in my own thoughts, I did not even realize that the Gestapo had returned. He began to speak. He told us that we were still young and therefore the great Reich, in its compassion, was forgiving us our mistake. He also told us that henceforth we should serve the great Reich and its Fuehrer.

A piece of paper—some sort of release form—was thrust into my hand. From a distance I heard a voice telling me that now I could go home.

With the cookie held tight in my hand, I staggered toward the exit. The daylight to which I was no longer accustomed blinded me temporarily. And then I started to run along the streets of Maribor toward my home, my home. . . . I opened my fist and swallowed the precious cookie.

The city was almost empty. Only here and there I met the retreating German army. They were all in rags and their carts were filled with the injured. I could not believe that I was free and that the hated green uniform was finally falling apart.

I rushed along the river Drava toward the east. I stopped only when the factories of the suburb of Melje were behind me. Before me I saw the houses of the first village outside the city. I was starved and exhausted. My vision blurred and suddenly everything disappeared before me. I wanted to keep my eyes open, to inhale the green of nature, the fresh air, the freedom, but I collapsed into pitch darkness.

When I awoke, there was a strange face leaning over me. I recognized the features of a farmer. He asked me what I was doing there, sleeping in the middle of the road. In seconds I told him my story and that I was on my way home. "For God's sake," he exclaimed, "you can't get home that fast. It's over sixty kilometers from here to your village." He warned me also that remnants of the German army, retreating under the assault of the Russians, were still in the vicinity. The front line—he said—was a mere hundred kilometers away. "Don't you hear the thunder in the east? You'd better come with me to my farm; you need food and we'll clean you up." And then he put me on his bicycle.

Beyond the town of St. Peter we reached his farm. His wife, his son, and his mother came running to greet us. Who was I, they wanted to know. Soon neighbors also crowded around me. "My God, my God!" they kept exclaiming. "Such a child and so cruelly tortured!"

Those wonderful people fed and pampered me like a baby. Nine days later the war was over.

* * *

(Twenty-five years later in Toronto)

The photographer's reception room was filled with people patiently waiting for their pictures. The photographer had suffered a heart attack and his wife had taken over. She busily bustled among the customers, apologizing for the delay. All the customers tried to comfort her, telling her that they would gladly wait and that everything was O.K.

When I entered, the photographer's wife, also a Slovenian, asked me to wait for her in her apartment behind the studio. "The wedding pictures of your daughter are beautiful!" she exclaimed. And after a while, "You'll have good company back there in my living room, with a Macedonian and a Slovenian. Have a nice talk until I finish my work."

The two gentlemen greeted me politely. They both rose from their seats.

That day I had a terrible toothache. I was holding my hand on my jaw. The Slovenian, a round bald-headed man about my age, noticed my discomfort and asked, "You have a toothache?"

I nodded.

"Here, have a glass of wine; it will help." He continued jokingly, "Wine is better medicine than aspirin. . . . So young and already you have decayed teeth?"

"No wonder," I defended myself. "When our teeth needed the best care we were in prison or in the concentration camps. Who got his teeth fixed in those days? And after the war it wasn't much better. We didn't have enough nutritious food. . . ."

"You were in prison?" he sighed.

"Oh, I was still very young then. It was during the war. I was fifteen. All that is so far away now. Sometimes I feel as if it all was just a dream."

"Just a moment," he jumped to his feet. "You were behind prison walls? Where? I think we have met somewhere before. . . . Were you in Maribor? On Sodna ulica?"

"Of course," I answered.

"Do you still remember . . . the bombardment in April, 1945?"

"Do I remember? That terrible day! How could I forget? How could I ever forget it?"

"Then you are . . . that lovely girl . . . from the cellar . . . the girl under my blanket?"

"And you are that handsome boy who gave me a cookie—a whole cookie! Yes, yes. . . ."

We joined our hands and looked at each other without saying a word.

"And we met again in Canada—at the other end of the earth. How strange our paths have been!"

"I would like to thank you again for that cookie. If I hadn't been so hungry then I would have kept it as a souvenir forever. I would put it into a treasure box, give it the best place in there. But. . . ."

"We were hungry, terribly hungry," he finished the sentence for me. We hurled questions at each other and waited impatiently for the answers: where and how had we been freed in 1945, how and why had we chosen Canada.

"Did you marry a Slovenian?"

"Of course, a survivor of our kind. Otherwise I could never be happy. It means a lot to me. We don't talk about the past very often anymore. We just think alike about it without even discussing it. I think that we are different from others who haven't had the same experience. The fears of the war which we carry in our hearts caused us to be estranged. We all feel the same pain—that we have never been young. . . . I still remember your words which sounded so terrifying in those days. You said we were old men and old women—do you still remember that?"

"Yes. And nowadays we even look old," he chuckled cheerfully. "Some who survived became drunkards but I ate a lot and lost all my hair. Just look at my belly. I was so afraid that I bought food and ate and ate. That old fear of ours that suddenly there won't be any food left is still in me. My cellar is filled with homemade sausages and hams. Since I took up hunting I even have a supply of venison stored away."

"I have a wife and two sons," he continued. "I am very happy that my sons are growing up in peace and enjoy a carefree youth. Everything that you and I never had."

He became thoughtful again. Then he asked, "Do you ever tell your daughters about the war and the deprivations of your youth?"

"Yes, sometimes. To them my accounts are like fairy tales. They can't comprehend. Nobody can if they haven't lived it themselves. . . . Were all those horrors and sufferings necessary for anybody? The question haunts me. Is it all only for history books? . . . Once upon a time there was the first World War . . . and then the second World War. . . . So many and so many people were killed. So many people were imprisoned and tortured. The Nazis were terrible. . . . But don't you think that history is repeating itself?"

"Let's forget about all that and drink wine to the miracle that kept us alive—even if it is sometimes hard for us to live with all our memories. You know, there are times when I feel guilty that I stayed alive. Why me, especially me?"

"The thought bothers me, too. Why didn't they kill me just before the end when they shot so many of our best people? . . . Why not me? . . . I also felt that I should hate mankind after my bitter experience. But it's just the opposite—I love them. Maybe just because once a human being helped me to stay alive. . . ."

New life, by H. Gregory Prusheck (Perušek)

"As we get older, there are more and more questions . . . and no answers," he remarked.

"I have a fear that I never felt in those days, perhaps because I didn't understand then. I often have the same dream: my home in the old country is a ruin, buried by bombs, and I am searching for my loved ones—always in vain. When I wake up, I am drenched with sweat. Many times I have touched myself, wondering if I am still alive, and I can feel the fear of all those twenty-five years which have passed. . . . Do you understand me?"

"Of course! Life is becoming easier now as I see that there are others like me still around, . . ." he said. "But one thing used to bother me all the time: on the jobs I had, every inflated little authoritarian, every impossible boss was like a Gestapo to me. I couldn't take them for long. Now I have finally won my independence—I have opened my own dental laboratory. If you want, I'll make you new teeth. You know, you have to eat well now that we can both have some food."

My feelings were a mixture of joy and sadness. At last I had met with my youth. . . .

Rose Mary Prosen

Rose Mary Prosen

LOOKING BACK

Looking back we do not remember
ourselves but the neighborhoods
we lived in and the things there we knew.
. . . How
much we belong to the past we learn
only when we have labored
to survive and prevail without it.

—Richard Howard
On the United States
Considered as a Landscape

Easter. Arising at four a.m. Standing at the gas stove in the kitchen while mother curled my hair with the curling irons. Wearing a long, loose white gown and gauze wings hooked onto my back; a crown of flowers on my head; a small white basket with a long curved handle in my hands, flower petals inside to strew in the aisles at church as I and my fellow angels marched, preparing the way for the Holy Monstrance, the robed priest, the altar boys, splendid in bright red cassocks, the incense burning and swinging on its chains; the organ and choir shaking our souls with Easter music. Who can forget the rich poetry of church ritual from her childhood days? It is not to be forgotten; never can be.

The church full of early morning men, their grimy, calloused hands scrubbed down with Lava soap; the aroma of garlic, cigars, of perspiration, of breath, not bad but *au naturel* (baking soda was our tooth powder); the women in their flowered straw hats, wearing their one good dress, their church dress; everyone wearing Sunday shoes, shining brightly, newly heeled; the choir announcing "Christ has risen as He said! Alleluia! Alleluia!" The triple brass bells ringing, alternating; brass bells on the left of the canopied tabernacle and on the right;

SOURCE: *Growing Up Slavic in America*, ed. Michael Novak (New York: EMPAC, 1976), 1-8. Reprinted by permission.

Dreams, by H. Gregory Prusheck (Perušek)

the clouds of incense stinging my eyes as I floated down the aisle. My sister girl angels and I led the whole procession; we emptied our little wooden baskets, strewing the whitesheeted center aisle with bright red and blue and yellow petals until we reached the front of the altar, where we stopped, turned, and watched the three priests ascend the steps, assisted by their altar boys, some of them, sometimes, missing a cue; whispers to Joey to move left, not right; to hold the priest's cape lower or higher.

The choir sang in English, the adopted language; the language their children were learning in the church school: English, the key to success; its correct pronunciation the mark of social distinction; its usage humiliating the old people, some of them illiterate, living their lives in devotion to Our Lady of Perpetual Help, chanting their rosaries at early evening; black babushkas, black dresses, widows, their faces creased in perpetual grief, sustaining themselves in plain chant in their own language, Slovenian, its very sounds striking the dim lit Friday evening services with assurance, with specificity; the communal spirit of women who had lost husbands, children, friends; who had buried babies, those too-many-born in times when the only birth-control was self-control; who had washed their own dead with their own hands in their own beds; who continued to plant lettuce, carrots, tomatoes, corn, beans; to nurture plum trees, pear trees, grape vines; to preserve these personal fruits and vegetables in Mason jars for the American winter; the old ladies of the neighborhood who in their devotion to the Blessed Virgin Mary and their own home, their kitchen, their cooking, preserved more than food and a religious tradition. Out of such single-minded routines arose the hope of a better life for their children, and the strength to endure another day in the family of strangers their children sometimes became. Better to keep holy the familiar paths than to wander in the wilderness, though they had boarded the great ship which had taken them across the Big Pond to a strange land where a peasant could dress like a gentleman if he could save the dollars to buy the suit that said he was such a man. Money. They came for money; money to buy the land that would mean they were no longer tenant farmers; that they were landlords; that they could nurture their own land and pass it on to their sons and grandsons, and nobody could take the land from them without war.

Through the years, I have had my quarrels with the Church, as I have had my quarrels with the world. Wanting to be me, I needed to find out what I was. Rebellious, confused, I left my home, my church, my neighborhood, and ventured forth into the world, into Cleveland, into America, into Europe, wondering where it was I belonged. I flowed into the mainstream, but sometimes the currents were too strong for me; the questions unanswerable. I drowned, and drowned, and drowned. In the ninth grade, a boy said to me, "You talk funny." I wondered what he meant. I listened to my friends, and I did not think they "talked funny." Then, that great American experiment, the public high school, opened my ears. I heard the English language spoken as I had never heard it spoken. At that time, a time without television, the high school was the only place to hear multiple dialects. There were some students, mostly Jewish, who spoke English as properly as it could be spoken in our school district. I began to hear that I did indeed pronounce my words differently, and so did my friends. I wrote a letter to a movie magazine. For twenty-five cents I could study the correct pronunciation of English words from a special publication, entitled, "How to Become an Actress." I practiced in secret, in the bathroom, of course, until I could pronounce the difficult "th" sound, which seemed the most distinctive and, therefore, the most necessary to conquer. How superior I felt when I had mastered this sound!

Of course, there were other language problems. Thanks to the Dominican nuns in our elementary school, I learned the grammar of the English language better than any professor was ever to teach it during my high school/college years. I still have those composition books where I learned to diagram sentences until I thought architecture was merely an extension of grammar! Those lessons are the lessons I myself teach today when I teach English grammar. I learned the rules of the language as I was to learn and love its sounds. Alas, however, I refused to speak Slovenian. What was a Slovenian? A hunkie. A greenhorn. A dumb Slav. "You sound like you just got off the boat," another boy had said to me once. I became ashamed that my parents spoke "funny"; that we laughed too loud; that we drank homemade wine; that our walls were wallpapered in flower patterns; that we grew our own vegetables; that my father raised chickens in our garage; that he constructed his children's beds out of scrap wood with his own hands; that he repaired all our shoes in our basement; that my mother never sat down to eat dinner with us (she cooked, served, ate when everyone was finished); that our clothes and our curtains and towels were homemade, some of them out of feed bags from the local granary; that stockings and worn clothing were never thrown away but given to my uncle who transformed them into rag rugs; that we had linoleum floors; and, I suspect, there were other more subtle aspects of that early life which I tried to reject but cannot remember.

What was to become of me? What became of most of the girls of that neighborhood in those days? Many of them went to work in factories at fifteen—the woolen mills, the lamp works. They became factory girls, glad to have a job, then a husband. Some of them became domestics. Without specific purpose, I finished high school, not the public high school. I transferred to a Catholic high school, Notre Dame Academy, after I had saved money for tuition. I was becoming an American, but I needed to be with my own kind, the safe structured world of Catholics. The language of my birth, Slovenian, did not pass my lips as I grew into womanhood. If someone did speak to me in that language, I might respond. More often, I would not. However, by the time I was thirteen, there had been five other children born, and my parents were outnumbered. We all spoke English. Except for Slovenian prayers, English dominated my family home and, of course, the elementary school. We had become Americans. My mother, whose parents were from Slovenia, spoke both languages. My father began to learn the English language, working in a brickyard and then in the steel mill. At home, he sat with me as I read my school books. He pronounced the sentences with me, word by word. We all became Americans, reading about Dick and Jane and "Run, Spot, run."

There were no Dicks or Janes in my neighborhood; there were many Josephs and Marys. In these strange first-grade readers, the children never went to church. There were no nuns nor priests nor wine nor polkas. Mrs. Dick & Jane did not preserve tomatoes for the winter. She and her husband never argued about money. Mr. Dick & Jane never got drunk. There was no saloon in the lives of this peculiar American family. Strangest of all, there were no flowers growing in their yard. They never mentioned flowers. In our school, every spring, the children sold seed packets. Every yard, small as some of them were, was filled with several different kinds of flowers, the most outstanding being the sunflower. I loved to look at the brightly colored illustrations on the seed packets. What I know today about flowers, I learned at St. Lawrence School and in the yards of its neighborhood. Men and women, saving nickels and dimes for the insurance man, always had a nickel for a packet of seeds. It is amazing to me today to list the flowers that grew in our family yard. The variety is so numerous a reader might imagine that we had an acre of land, but we did not. We had a small city lot. In it grew marigolds, roses, lilies-of-the-valley, petunias, forget-me-nots, daffodils, geraniums, irises, nasturtiums, sweet peas, and morning glories against the wooden fence. Oh, yes, there were also glorious peonies! My parents planted and cared for all these flowers as naturally as eating and sleeping. I never once heard the word "landscaping." I was astonished to learn years later that some people actually bought full-grown flowers from a business called a "nursery" and paid a perfect stranger to dig up their yards. How strange to deny themselves the pleasure of watching a seed sprout into a beautiful blossom! Perhaps it was then I began to suspect that mine was a peasant's heritage tied to the land and the fruit thereof. Imagine raising rabbits as well as chickens in a city garage! Today, I am sure the neighbors would object. Then, the neighbors, too, had their chickens and rabbits, if only two or three. I remember the smell of chicken blood in

Slovenian peasant women, by Lillian Brulc

the basement after my father had wrung a chicken's neck, then chopped off its head. Chickens do run around without their heads! No chicken today tastes like the chickens my mother cleaned and prepared for Sunday dinner. There is no chicken soup in America today like the chicken soup my mother made from our home grown chickens. Homemade noodles went with the home-made soup. My sister and I hung around the kitchen table as my mother floured the cutting board, rolled out the dough and chopped the noodles. The flour clung to our aprons and dusted the floor. Even our eyelashes fluttered flour dust. Dick and Jane's mother never made her own chicken soup. Neither did her children have the pleasure of watching her chop homemade noo-dles.

After food and flowers, I remember most of all music. My parents bought a used player piano and, at age seven, I signed up at the Dominican convent to take piano lessons. How proud I and my family were when I wore the blue satin blouse and red plaid skirt my mother made me for my first recital. In the basement of the church, the neighborhood gathered to see what their children had been up to all that school year. There was accordion music, of course, folk dancing, colors, dramatic reci-tations in Slovenian and English. Afterwards, the adults re-viewed their children's performances in Slovenian, while the children reviewed themselves in English. The old folks looked on and wept. What they must have seen, I suspect, is the begin-ning of the end of their way of life; a discomfort more acute than age and ailing naturally bring; a discomfort that signified social change, for with money and education came social mobil-ity. Who would respect the woman who wore her money in a little bag around her neck; who boiled bones for soup to nourish her family of eight; who took in boarders in every room in the house, including the kitchen; who boiled and laundered shirts on a washboard in her kitchen when she wasn't peeling, or canning, or baking, or ironing; who never bought a paper product because old newspapers served just as well? Who could respect her hag-gling ways, her sharp tongue when the Jewish peddler arrived at her door, carrying his suitcase stuffed full of life's luxuries? A penny too much was a penny wasted! Even rags had market value. On Saturdays came the horse and wagon and a skinny man who collected rags and paper. "Paper-rags! Paper-rags!" he would shout, and the ladies of the neighborhood would hurry out, their fingers shaking as they received their pennies. What child could understand then that terrible struggle to pay the mortgage before anything; that fierce desire to own the land and a house thereon; to owe no one; to be free and clear? I cer-tainly did not.

At the same time, a Sunday did not pass without some money being placed in the collection basket at Mass. Pennies and nickels and dimes built the church and school, the national home, and, of course, a bank. In a time when workers had meager, if any, unemployment compensation and inadequate hospitalization benefits; a time when the welfare system had yet to be defined; at such a time, a generation of men and women from Central Europe determined to survive and make a better life for their children. They did so, and in their doing, they forged steel and wove woolens, assembled lamps and mixed paint; they manned the factories of America which have made us today the most prosperous people in the history of the world. Today our garbage cans are extravagantly full. Our pets eat better than did some of our ancestors. Surely, somewhere in heaven the old ladies in black babushkas are shaking their heads at the sight of our waste.

So I remember the men and women of my neighborhood; the factory whistles, announcing the eight-hour shifts; the men in their steel-toed shoes, their blue denim clothes heavy with grease, their lunch buckets empty, giving me a piece of candy as they passed our house walking home from the mills. What were their names? One was Matt; one was Cy. My father coming home; my mother filling the bathtub with hot water; listening to Gabriel Heater's news on the radio; boiling the greasy work clothes in a copper tub in the basement; hearing the train whistle and chug; calling out to the train conductor, "Gimme some chalk." My father and I walking in the center of the tracks, picking up coal. The women in the grocery store, pointing to sides of beef, or pork, picking out that evening's meal; the sausage house where the butcher smoked his special brand of sausage; watching the blood and fat and meat chips being ground through the giant grinder into casings; the smell of sawdust on the store's floor; my mother, carrying her paper shopping bags as she walked up the street to our house; the icebox in our hallway which could hold fifty pounds of ice, although we would buy only twenty-five when we did buy any; the fish truck, stinking and loaded with crushed ice and Lake Erie blue pike on Fridays. Our lives had rhythm: fish on Fridays, chicken on Sundays. Saturday nights for baths. And what were vacations for? Why, painting the house, repairing the sidewalk or stairs, scrubbing, rubbing, scouring. In their entire lives, my parents never had a vacation. Yet, I do not remember self-pity. It was enough to have a sturdy, neat house and healthy children. It was more than enough. Such was their source of pride. Such was the simple life of my childhood days, or so it seems to me now. I am beginning to feel there is gold in the dust that I sift as I write these words; a pagan spirit, beyond any language, that is my heritage, tempered by thrift and work. Of course, no one was perfect, but the strong took care of the weak. The retarded, the mad, the deformed, the illegitimate—none of these were sent away. Families cared for their own, accepting these burdens as fatalistically as rain and thunder. The drunken, the desperate, the stupid—these, too, fit into the community of workers. The old and the young and the middle-aged shared households, each leaning on each as circumstances required. The Church stood at the center of all our lives, the priests burdened beyond confessionals to guide the young and console the old, to straddle two worlds, Slovenia and America; somehow, to strike a meeting ground for three generations of souls.

My generation became American. Not until I was out of high school did I begin to ask, "What is an American?" When a stranger asked me, "What is your nationality?" I always answered, "Slovenian," though I had been born in Cleveland, as had my mother and father. All my grandparents were from Slovenia. My father was to return there at the age of three when his father decided he would not make America his family's home. That grandfather died in Franz Josef's cavalry during World War I, age thirty-eight. My grandmother sent her son to America to avoid conscription and to find employment in 1922. She sold a cow to finance his ocean voyage, and sent her eldest son to Cleveland. She was never to see him again.

When grandmother died, in her eighties, a photographer recorded her village funeral. The men, and women, and children she had known all her life carried her to her churchyard grave within walking distance of her home. No automobiles. No hearse. Only people and flowers. Frances. *Frančiska*. She had lived the lonely widow's life, never to see her grandchildren, for she had sent her second son to U.S. Steel in Cleveland, also. One stayed with her. I saw her grave in 1965 in Dolensko, in the churchyard of Sts. Cosmos and Damian. I lit one candle and placed it in the earth before her tombstone. Frances, I thought, what a hard life! I remembered her letters. What were her words? I had the photographs—her deep eyes and patient frown, her gnarled hands, worker's hands. Frances, I have come to greet you! From a factory town, from the shadows of steel mills, I kneel before your tombstone. My eyes look up to see the mountains of your life—those mountains which I had described to me as a little girl from my father's memory. I felt at home. In your house I saw the same picture of St. Cecelia playing at her organ mounted on your wall—the same picture my mother had mounted on our wall. I had studied piano. I had received the family gift of music.

An ox startled me out of my reverie, and I arose and walked out of the churchyard, across the bridge, and up the path to the house that was my heritage. A sturdy house rooted to the earth, it seemed. Sleeping that night in the old house, I dreamed the songs of my childhood, songs my father had taught me; songs the children at the elementary school sang in concert every spring, directed by that great spirit, Ivan Zorman, our church musical director. Songs about mountains, horses, flowers, boys and girls, lovers, winning or losing. At dawn, I stirred and

A village of Dolenjska, Slovenia, by H. Gregory Prusheck (Perušek)

listened to the swishing sounds of workers. I got up, looked out the window and saw a man and a boy, cutting the tall grass, rhythmically, their scythes glinting in the early morning sun. It was another world. Was I awake? Yes. It was 1965, but motors had not yet invaded this village in Dolensko. Later, in the attic, I saw a spinning wheel and a few ceramic pots, used, I was told, by attaching to long poles. Then, they were thrust into the stove below, which was furnace as well as hearth and oven.

In one giant leap, a country peasant had become the city steel worker.* What were his dreams at night? How many mornings did he arise to walk in the dark to the mill where he earned the money to buy his bread, bread that he had once made with his own wheat? What transformations blazed within his soul? Some men drank. The corner saloon on Friday and Saturday nights was always full—their time for psychoanalysis and their time for remembering home. Some felt displaced their whole life long, never learning English, never leaving the neighborhood, hugging their own blood, their own plot of land, living still as workers on the landlord's great estate. They knew their boundaries—the lines their children crossed and crossed. The price for bread was high.

On Easter, 1976, I will remember the blessing of the basket; the ritual meal of colored eggs, baked ham, homemade bread, fresh horseradish, sausage and homemade wine; the sparkling windows of our house, the clean curtains, floors, walls and woodwork; all of us singing for the Great Feast Day; the sidewalks and porches hosed down; the yards raked, ready for seeding; the great basso voice of Mr. Snyder in the church choir, shaking the statues, the parishioners, the very earth, stirring roots, arousing the spirits of our ancestors in that Slovenian-American village in Newburgh. In my memory, his voice stirred the winds of the Asian steppes, raised questions: who are these, my people, my soul? The great Slavonic heart of a people dispersed and made singular through war and time and the elements; one tribe to settle in Cleveland, Ohio, to become again new men and women. I, too, am new.

---

*Between 1880 and 1914, when emigration from Slovenia to America was at its peak, Slovenia was still a predominantly agricultural country. According to current statistics, only twenty percent of Slovenians are engaged in agriculture, while the remaining four-fifths derive their livelihood from industry, mining, tourism, and other non-agricultural occupations.

Planting, by Lillian Brulc

II

GIVE US TODAY OUR DAILY BREAD

Ivan Molek (1882–1962)

Ivan Molek

GRAVEYARDS OF THE LIVING

Translated by Mary Molek

Sunday came and Tony and John started the night shift in the new mine. The night-shift work week went from Sunday midnight to Saturday midnight.

On Monday the foreman sent Tony to a small new pit in Shaft 75. There, machine drilling was proceeding on a slant through a great layer of rock to a vein of copper. Already, some three hundred feet had been cleared. It was the job of the night shift to remove all of the rock which the day crew had dug out so that the next day's drilling and blasting could proceed.

Two other men were sent into the hole with Tony, a Slovenian, and a greenhorn Italian who understood not a word of English. All three were to load at the bottom of the pit. The motor at the top, run by a young boy, dropped the empty three-ton tramcar on a cable, down a track, to the bottom of the pit where it was loaded, hauled back, and dumped.

The task, though simple, was not easy. Ventilation at the bottom of the new excavation was so poor that, even when they sat quietly, the miners were covered with sweat. The foreman, an efficient man, had sent down three workers so that they could alternate without destroying the rhythm of the work process. Two of them loaded while the third, who had ridden to the top on a full car, rested and cooled off until the next car came up. Then he returned in the empty tram to exchange places with one of the others.

Other than this crew, Shaft 75 was deserted. The long shaft was as quiet and peaceful as a graveyard, except for the whine of the distant motor. And it smelled like a sepulchre, too. Even the fat-bellied rats, companions in any mine, had long since deserted this one. The once light-brown walls of the shaft now reflected black in the light of the tallow lamps

SOURCE: Ivan Molek, *Dva svetova* (Chicago: Prosvetna Matica, 1932), 122-26.

Labor, by H. Gregory Prusheck (Perušek)

set on the miners' hats. Far off, the hollow groaning water pump in the lower pits hooted like a melancholy owl.

Tony was not happy to be sent to this smoked-up hole, but he would be there for only one night and he easily shook off his depression. He and the Slovenian were the first to jump into the empty car for the trip down into the mine. The timberman had managed to fit only two-thirds of the shaft with a wooden ceiling and sides. A thick plank was nailed transversely across the passage where they had stopped. A full tramcar could pass through easily but a man riding on it would have to bend low to get by. Tony pointed this out to his companion as they went past it.

At the bottom of the pit the miners removed their thick woolen shirts, stripped to the waist, and went to work. Soon shovels sang as they quickened their pace. When the car was loaded, Tony told his partner to get on it, pulled the wire, and the cable hauled load and miner to the top. Wiping his sweaty hands and chest with a rag, Tony sat down on a rock to wait for the empty car with the Italian passenger to come clattering back.

When the swarthy man arrived, Tony tried to warn him about the dangerous plank, but the newcomer only looked at him wide-eyed and repeated, "Parla niente." What a nuisance! They filled the iron box in silence. Perhaps, thought Tony, it might be a good idea for both of them to ride to the top this first time. If he couldn't explain the danger to his companion, he would demonstrate what to watch out for. By the time the cart was loaded, it was clear that his partner was exhausted; sweat poured off him and his lungs pumped like a blacksmith's bellows.

Tony sat the Italian down at the front of the car, settled beside him, gave the signal for the ascent, and the tram began to roll upwards. Again, by word and action, Tony tried to convey the imminent danger to the silent passenger, but with no success; the man sat there rigid, tense, and uncomprehending. The car gathered speed and soon was but a few feet from the plank.

At the last moment, Tony grabbed his partner's head to force it out of the way of the dangerous barrier. But he had moved too quickly—he lost his balance and slipped from the tramcar onto the tracks ahead.

It all happened in an instant. Tony was wedged up to his hips under the vehicle. He lay on his side, scraping against the jagged rock and the wooden-platformed tracks as the car moved forward. The Italian jumped off the side of the car, picked himself up with lightning speed despite some scratches and began to howl like a wounded beast. He tugged at the wire madly, hoping to stop the cart. But the dull-witted youth at the top had set the motor at full speed and was oblivious to everything but the whine of the machinery.

Still life, by H. Gregory Prusheck (Perušek)

The tramcar dragged Tony with it in its progress up the steep gradient. He was fully conscious but felt no pain from the skin and flesh torn from his hands by the sharp rock. It was like swimming in a huge black horn. Sparks from the cart's iron wheels flashed along the tracks. A booming din echoed around him as though the roof, immense cliffs, the entire mine were caving in. . . .

His predicament was clear. If the track were free, the tramcar could pull him to the top still alive. But he knew that the track was not free. . . . At any moment now the cart would reach the wooden cylinder around which the cable wound. There was only a few inches of space between car and cylinder. Yes, death awaited him there. . . . He would be crushed.

He was certain that this was his end. Only moments remained before death. What should he think about in these last few seconds? How should he make use of them? Was it worth thinking at all any more?

Tony's mind flashed back through his life, as much of it as he remembered since his childhood. All the images, as clear and as vivid as the most crystalline reality, passed before him. The old country, mother and sister in the little hut on the outskirts of the village—perhaps the cellar has been repaired by now so it no longer leaks—the neighbor's Kate, Stanishar and Louisa, the struggle of the little people . . . the departure at night, Vienna, Prague, Bremen, the ocean, New York . . . Steelton, Frank Zamershnik, the factory, the slaughter of the Black, Anna Shoster . . . Reading, Pennsylvania, escape and tramping, Bill, Pittsburgh . . . the fat woman saloonkeeper, the Salvation Army, the strike, the revolutionary Shartz, Ruthy . . . Chicago, Calumet at the end of the earth, Sajovec and the Wizard's Apprentice, Shvigel, Robkar and Fannie . . . Saloonkeeper Feer and the job he offered in the best mine on earth. . . .

Little and much. He had experienced little and much. . . . Still young, he had seen and met with two worlds. . . . He could see, experience, and meet with even more—a pity that he would not. . . . Did he fear death? No, not really. When a person is born he is destined to die. But when a man is still young and vigorous, when he likes to work and still has much undone work before him, why must he die? . . . Especially here in this devil of a hole so deep underground, in this graveyard of living people three hundred feet under the surface. . . .

There is still a moment! . . .

Aha, the end! . . .

A million sparks flashed around him. They combined into a small flame which grew smaller and smaller until only one spark remained. Soon, this spark, too, vanished. All that was left was the infinite darkness of nothingness. . . .

Ivan Dolenc

Ivan Dolenc

NIGHT SHIFT IN THE BAKERY

They gathered gradually in front of the long, white-black plant, like bubbles upon shaken dough. One came near, then another—no two men arrived together to this one-way, dead-end street. Yonge Street, the "Queen of Toronto," was quickly dimming in the near distance, and, beyond, the stars were flickering one after another like shiny drops appearing on bread crusts in the overheated oven.

Few men stopped at the huge entrance; they all hesitated. They savored their last breath of cool air before stepping into the hot hell. They chewed on their cigarettes or pipes, greeted each other with a swing of their arms and listened to the noise of the congested city in the distance.

The bakery was located in the heart of the city, but no cars or neatly-dressed people came this way. No happy faces could be seen here either—one could only see the subdued and the silent and the tired. Now all of them enjoyed seriously the phony eternity of those last few minutes before that automatic punch of the time clock upon their workers' cards.

All of them were now leaning against the wall of the plant; only Nikolay sat alone at the edge of the street on the opposite side. The grayish wise man was remembered for the remark he uttered on that postwar day when they were lined up in the plant office offering themselves for the night shift.

"There are no friends left—nor are there any enemies," he blurted out loudly as he glanced around at the long row of applicants before and behind him. "Only competitors have remained!" Nikolay's words, spoken in his soft Russian-English, sounded so aristocratic and out of place in the deadly monotony of the plant that they all burst into laughter.

"Everyone here is on his own and forever alone," he continued, paying not the slightest attention to his listeners. "Anyone with a family, like myself, is doubly and triply aware of this. So don't expect me to give up in this long line and perhaps get lost on the street! I need the night shift for my

Prepared especially for this anthology.

Evening clouds, by Ted Kramolc

survival!" His directness at once evoked much sympathy from the others. They named him their "Saint."

On this late evening in June, there were some twenty or thirty men standing on the street, but not one of them entered the plant just yet. They waited on and stirred only when they heard a bus pull to a stop on the main street. Although they heard the bus every evening, they seldom saw it in the twilight. But when a tall, broad-shouldered gentleman carrying an attache case stepped off the bus, they knew that the time had come for their departure for the plant locker rooms in the basement of the block-long building. Janosh was always more accurate than the watches on their wrists. He approached slowly and greeted them with a wave of his briefcase—it was exactly nine forty-five!

Like most of the others, Janosh was no longer young. They called him the "Professor." Again, such a name was nothing extraordinary on the night shift crew, for there was not a single professional baker or professional laborer among them. The crew was undoubtedly the best-educated team of its kind to be found between the Atlantic and the Pacific—on the Canadian side. It consisted of European professors, engineers, economists, doctors of humanities, physicians, teachers, artists, lawyers, army officers, diplomats, and, of course, all of them former celebrities. They represented all Slavic countries and were also joined by Estonians, Latvians, and Lithuanians. All the rest were students who attended daytime classes.

Although at times they referred to themselves as "The Brain Trust of the United Immigrants," normally, by unspoken agreement, they avoided all references to political or social labels. The differences among them were so great, especially in political background, that had they not done so, they would not have been able to spend one single night together in peace. Without exception, they had marinated, mayonnaised and glazed themselves according to the lovely old recipe called tolerance. One night Mike, the young theology student, described the exemplary behavior of the night shift with a quote from a cookbook. To the great satisfaction of all present he cited the following paragraph:

"Game, especially the meat of an old field rabbit, must be marinated so that it loses its toughness and can be preserved for an extended period of time. We do not recommend marinating the meat of young deer, for in the process it loses much of its nourishing components and its natural taste."

All recognized the thrust of the recipe but no one was offended by it. With understanding they swallowed the truth from the book of good cuisine and reacted with self-knowing laughter.

At midnight, the group headed by the Polish literary historian Henry stopped the conveyor belt that carried the American and fruit bread down to the ground floor. Eight sweaty intellectuals in white uniforms sat down around him, each with a paper cup of coffee in hand, ready to listen to his lecture. Tonight the topic was "The Tragic in World Literature."

"From the bottom of my heart I would like to follow the ideal path of Prince Myshkin," Henry ceremoniously concluded his comparison. "But I see that this path of the heart, this way of integrity and noblemindedness, of humanitarianism and respect, leads only to a bakery of dreams like this one here." He gulped some coffee, then continued. "We are acting out the miserable role of Ganya; we are satisfied with the leftovers and the big world out there is still the world of the Rogozhins and Ptitsyns! As for myself, I readily admit that I cannot follow those two natures, despite the fact that I could easily reach them or even outdo them with my reason. The unhappiness of their life is attainable, this I know; even so, I would rather forego dirty competition of that sort and wait."

There was a break in the discussion. The listeners sipped their coffee, searching for an answer to the problem presented to them. First to speak was Frank, the Estonian artist.

"There is no answer," he said. "Isn't it enough that Myshkin came from a sanatorium for the insane and in the end again returned to a sanatorium?"

"True," nodded another as he took an apple pie out of the refrigerator. "Myshkin cannot be followed. His kind of goodness leads to suicide."

"He remained as lonely as Christ with his experiment," stressed Martin, a former Catholic priest who had married a year ago. "Christ, too, has not a single honest disciple or follower left in our commercialized world—only admirers remain."

"But still, I see a minor difference here," laughed Mike openly. "Myshkin is not a legend so it isn't possible to make money on him as the organized profiteers do in the name of the Nazarene."

"Let's end on this point for tonight," said Henry. He turned to a Lithuanian Doctor of Politics and suggested, "Perhaps you can continue next time. Until Wednesday, on our behalf, you can consider if similar dough has risen in 'Hamlet' and in the sad 'Knight from Mancha.'"

"O.K.," answered Ignatius, "I'll do my homework."

Then all of them rose, returned to the baking ovens, and the indefatigable assembly line began to hum again.

* * *

Dragolyub, a graduate economist, was placing cakes destined for shipment to chain stores into the steel cabinets. Every night, as he set them in the containers, he exercised his memory by recalling the first names of all the great personalities or scenes of the beautiful places they were named after. He always began with the Elizabeth and Napoleon cakes, then continued with those of Linz, Brazil, Italy, Florence, Hamburg, and Panama. Only after he had carefully pushed the Indian cakes onto the tray did he count the mundane rum, orange, coffee, marble cakes, and the others. When he got to the nut, strawberry, and blueberry cakes he contemplated longer and began to count them more slowly, as if he were dwelling on something from the past. His tired eyes behind spectacles began to close involuntarily and he was forced to rest. His colleagues, shuffling their feet, stood before the cabinets with the large white order sheets pasted on the doors. Dragolyub turned to them, leaned against the wagon with the cakes, and shouted loudly:

"People of God, I won't be in this purgatory much longer! In the autumn I am leaving you!"

They descended on him from all sides and stared at him, wide-eyed.

"Are you joking?" the first one queried. He helped himself to broken pieces of Colonial cake, which lay on a special tray for waste, and sat down beside Dragolyub on the hot floor.

"No, I'm not joking," replied the young economist. "My mathematical problem will soon be solved—maybe in one week or two—and then Monte Carlo is mine!"

"May I visit you someday?" eagerly inquired the Estonian teacher who, as a French Legionnaire, had swum out of Dien Bien Phu. "Ah, but will you and your wife still want to know me?"

In addition to his night work, during the day Dragolyub worked in a large supermarket alongside his wife—she was a cashier and he was a stock clerk. All of their savings were invested in autumn and winter tickets for the French Riviera. They had already been there three times and on the last occasion Dragolyub had won small sums at the roulette table. He was convinced that he was close to discovering a sure betting system that would win him a fortune.

"I have borrowed several thousand," he continued excitedly, "and I'm hoping for a clean sweep. I'm going to break the Bank!" He wiped off his moist glasses and went on, "And then I'm going to call myself a capitalist. I might even buy this bakery of ours, if only to make it cooler for you fellows."

"And you won't work nights any longer?" called a man from the other side of the shop. He had three children and a sickly wife at home. He had enrolled at a Canadian university but could not afford the costs.

"Nights?" thundered the passionate gambler. "I won't work days, either! Do you understand what this means in North America? . . . I will be free, free at last! I'll have money and again I'll be a respectable intellectual. It's quite possible that I may want to become a human being again, too. A 'Man' with a capital 'M' who is completely hot or completely cold—and never lukewarm again as all of us here are. Have you ever heard of anything good that came from a lukewarm disposition?"

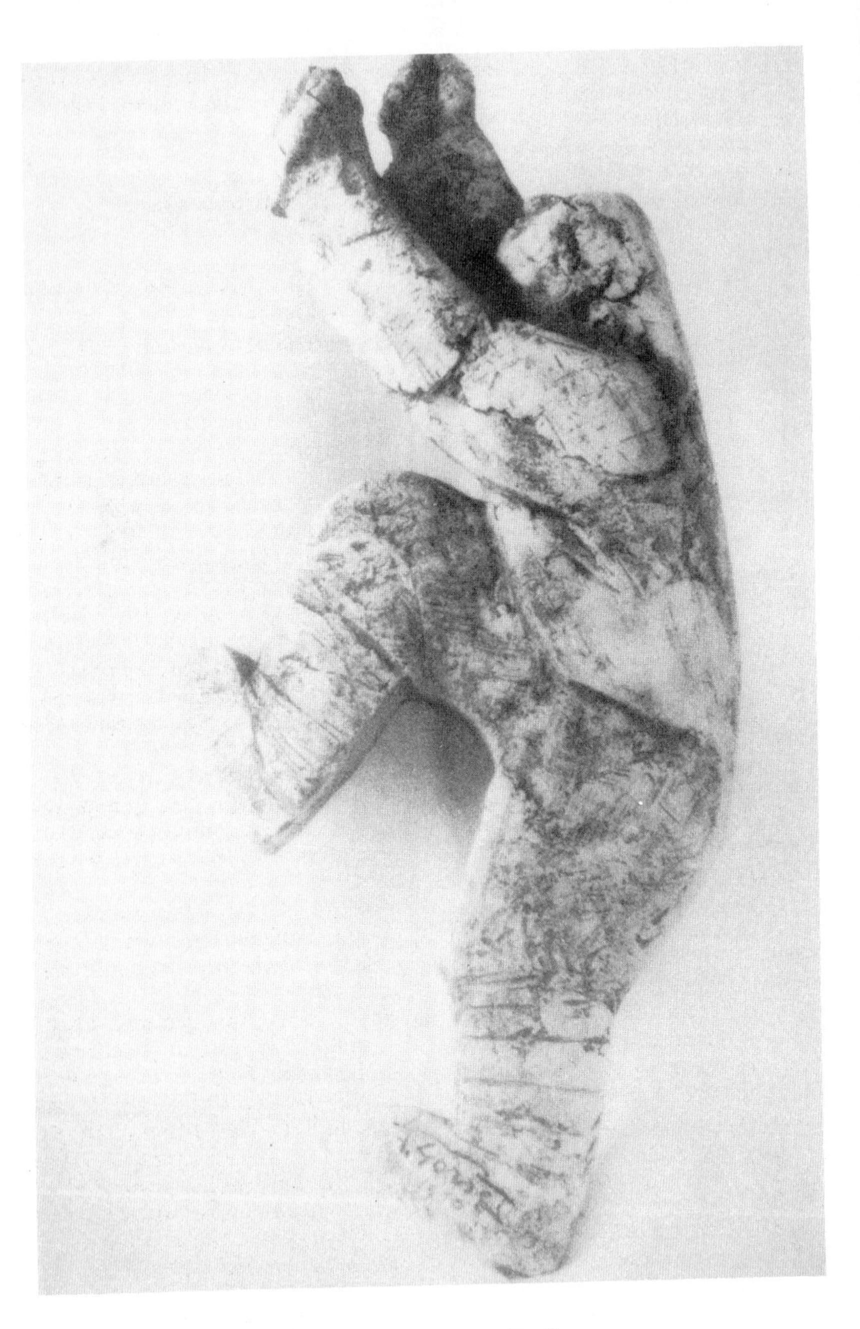

Climber, by France Gorše

"This bakery of dreams has burned him terribly," old Vassily thought in sympathy, as he recalled his own dreams in the prisoner-of-war camp; but he said nothing.

Several shouts were heard:

"Lucky fellow!"

"At least somebody is getting out of here!"

"Congratulations!"

"A mathematical genius!"

The economist was suddenly frightened by the effect of his revelation and he desperately wanted to return to his cakes as soon as possible. His colleagues dispersed slowly; each fell to his own work.

* * *

Janosh ran over the cement loading dock where trucks came and left again throughout the night. His job was to unload the huge boxes of poppyseed buns which arrived from other plants, and to fill the steel cabinets with the cookies and pastry which descended in painfully assorted dozens from the floors above. Over and over he repeated the Czech names for all the eighters, twists, half-moons, boats, raisins, slices, drops, puffs, tarts, macaroons, animal and chocolate-chip cookies, as he had done at three o'clock in the morning for many years. He continued with Neapolitans, peanut butter crunch cookies, shortbreads, marshmallows and doughnut holes. Here and there he nibbled something from a tray.

Along the loading platform other intellectuals, their faces marked by a European mildness, helped him. The group included four lawyers, two diplomats, a physician, and three engineers. All had arrived in this country too old to have any hope of ever leaving the bakery.

Janosh was respected and admired by his co-workers, not just because he was the oldest but because he was a living encyclopedia of the humanities—a philosopher, linguist, historian, and poet, all in one.

The crew worked in the fresh air, so it was natural that they were constantly taunted that they were enjoying paradise while the others suffered and sweated in the hell of the open ovens or in the purgatory of the airless second floor which had no windows or doors, just the elevator and the dull gray steel of the sorting cabinets. Janosh invariably answered these jibes with the explanation that this was true only in the summer. In winter, in the cold slush and snow, the established order of things was reversed and he and his men were in purgatory and sometimes, when the snowstorms whistled, even in hell—if only in a Miltonian frigid hell.

The night was clear and full of the mysterious light of the moon and the glowing stars. It was a night worthy of Goethe. Although Janosh continued collecting French and Spanish biscuits and rolls on his way, his thoughts rose faster than the yeastiest dough and connected into sentences in his mind. The bakers in the plant all agreed that he not only wrote well but that he was truly a great poet. They and his wife were his only critics.

He wrote articles, essays, and poems for himself, for the night shift, and for his understanding mate. Once a month he collected the sheets covered with typewritten lines and tied them into bundles. Often he sent such a bundle to the address of so-and-so or so-and-so, countrymen whom he had met at church or on a streetcar, but rarely did he get a response. To be perfectly honest, he never really expected anything to come from these efforts of his. They were refreshing to his colleagues on the night shift and they were satisfying to his wife. But mainly, he had to continue his writing if he wanted to remain alive.

In one of these bundles he outlined a calm, Tolstoyan appraisal of his situation. Perhaps, one day, someone may find it and discover the inner truth of the bakery people.

In his tract Janosh maintained that an intellectual should not waste time and emotion if he does not get an echo. He should acknowledge, once and for all, that the nucleus of this continent is a never-ending domain of elegantly dressed servants and maids to whom any idea other than winning their bread is not only strange but hostile. Here he added that he would not bother to probe the question of whether winning one's bread could be classified as a human idea.

On the same page he continued, "When these people realize that they are in the majority, they will close down humanitarian institutions and unleash all of their police and military apparatus against those who dare to defend anything but personal material comfort."

On this night Janosh was absorbed in kneading out a poem about a man who saw no relationship between his personality and warm baskets and boxes which he was transferring from hand to hand at three o'clock in the morning. Certain parts of the poem burned him more than the trays hot from the oven. He served these nameless trucks only because he needed a small sum of money every Friday morning for another week of existence. There could be no other explanation for this dreary nightly ceremony. But his poem was concerned with living, suffering people who were awaiting his bakery colleague, the physician; he saw wild waters without bridges which could be tamed easily by his colleagues, the engineers. Through his words there surged a flood of precious, lost, discarded human time which was already a deluge of biblical proportions.

Janosh stopped with this thought and stared, perplexed, into the reality around him. Half-empty trucks still stood at the dock. And alongside him men were working with an enthusiasm normally reserved for the rescue of a drowning person. Blazing heat, smelling of bread in all its forms, still hit out unbearably from the plant. Loud shouts could be heard. "The night shift is probably announcing the morning coffee break," Janosh said to himself. He, too, put aside everything he held in his hands and in his thoughts.

Humiliated and bent from the long night's work, he had forgotten himself that he was still an intellectual from time to time. Inwardly, unwillingly, he had hung a white flag which waved to the order of the plant just as the flame in the long, deep bread oven.

"Only till six, only till six," he murmured and once again embraced the shrinking pie of the moon and the fading points of the stars above him, which were becoming recognizably smaller and paler, and then he stepped out from the yard under the roof of the plant.

* * *

The sun had already been smiling for an hour over the street, when from the huge entrance door the nightly bakers rushed onto the sidewalk. They all hurried in one direction, toward the main street of the city. They looked neither left nor right; they did not stop; they even forgot to smoke. And they did not turn either.

Nikolay, the grayish wise man, was the only one running alone on his own side of the street. No one paid any attention to him; no one remembered his saying that "everyone here is on his own and forever alone."

Frank Bukvich

Frank Bukvich

SWEEPER MARICH

Translated by Edward Krasovich

If I hadn't been transferred to the paint shop, I probably never would have become acquainted with him. In the paint shop I felt that I knew the man before I actually saw him. My fellow employees apprised me of him at the very moment I arrived; it seemed that they could hardly wait until I got there to tell me, as if on my first day in the paint shop I would have nothing to occupy my mind except the character of a lowly janitor. This janitor was the one and only Marich, who had fled from the Monarchy to America to avoid being drafted sometime before the first World War.

In the shop there was utter confusion. One worker recalled one thing, another remembered something else, until they were all talking at the same time and I didn't know which one I should listen to. During the recounting they gestured expansively and laughed boisterously. At first I didn't believe them, not because I thought they were joking with me, a novice, or because I thought they were putting me on. I simply could not believe that such a character as Sweeper Marich existed or could have existed.

"Now he is on the third floor. At 8:20 he will appear on the second floor. He will reach us here on the ground floor at twenty minutes to ten," said Herbie, as I looked in vain throughout the shop for Marich.

"Just look how much dirt there is under that table! It takes an expert to sweep only in the middle of the room," said the first Polack.

"The broom handle is too short for him to reach under the table," chimed in the second Polack, the brother of the first. "He scolds all of us for not being concerned enough about cleanliness. You will be included, too."

SOURCE: Frank Bukvich, "Pometač Marich," *Meddobje*, vol. 2, no. 6, 1956, 286-88.

The discourse was interrupted by the buzzer summoning us to begin work. Time went by quickly that day. I did not need to look at the clock; just a glance at the shop entrance immediately told me that it was twenty minutes to ten. There at the door stood Marich, his chin resting on hands wrapped expertly around the top of the broom handle. That this awkward, baldheaded figure swathed in a dirty apron was Sweeper Marich would have been apparent even if he had come in without a broom, for his officious eyes scanned the floor tyrannically as if gathering scattered dirt. After the first fleeting glance, I was convinced that here was a born loafer who could take a full eight hours to sweep this paint shop which actually required barely an hour's work. It was clear that Marich was not merely carrying out the duties of his job in a shop but was engaged, day after day, in playing an important role, more suitable for a theatrical stage than for a shop. The way he held his broom was in itself worthy of recognition: the upper part lay in his left palm as though he were grasping someone by the neck; his right hand rested somewhat toward the center of the handle. His bearing, though artificial in the extreme, was at the same time familiarly natural. It was sincerely genuine yet calculatingly deceitful—that peak of an artist's skill, rare even on the legitimate stage, when the actor's performance so charms the spectator that it takes his breath away or brings him to tears.

Glancing at the spot where the floor was unswept, Marich bristled and turned his piercing eyes, showering fire and brimstone, onto the unfortunate individual who happened to be working nearby. "This fellow is new; it will be necessary to teach him about cleanliness," his eyes seemed to scold me. Involuntarily, I looked down—there under the table I noticed two crumpled pieces of paper protectively surrounding a long cigarette butt. I fully expected Marich to descend on me with a reprimand but he did not. He just stood there at the entrance, not making a move as he gazed at me, not angrily yet not pleasantly. His look, at best, expressed curiosity. After a while he moved slightly and greeted the employees near the entrance with a loud "Good morning." He waited until they returned the greeting, then resumed leaning on the broom. He was frozen in that stance for a good quarter of an hour. His benumbed, almost dead countenance reminded me of Rodin's statue, The Thinker. Only his eyes were alive, taking pleasure in the sight of the employees feverishly working to meet their quotas.

Finally, he pulled himself erect in a movement so gradual that one felt he was straightening an iron bar in his spine. Clinging awkwardly to the broom, he bent forward imperceptibly and began to sweep very slowly, as if he were facing a week's work for which he must conserve his strength.

At first I thought he was so slow because his blood had not yet warmed up. But to my great surprise, I soon noticed that Marich was actually most agile at the onset of his sweeping. After that his movements became slower and less frequent, until the sweep of the broom moved no faster than the minute hand on a clock. Finally, I could detect no movement of the broom whatsoever. I surmised that Marich was still sweeping since he was bent forward in the customary sweeping posture. At last the broom made one final forward thrust, like a flame before it dies, and stopped. It was quite clear that the sweeper did not stop the broom; it had stopped of its own accord. The sweeper seemed to be so tired that he was barely able to stop himself, much less the broom. Marich leaned on the broom and rested. For a fleeting instant it seemed to me that the broom in his hands had become something else, but I could not guess what it might be.

I looked at the clock. Marich had swept a distance of barely two yards from the doorway in five minutes. Having observed his lassitude, I now became more conscious of the broom than of the sweeper. I began to wonder when it would glance at the clock and remind Marich to start sweeping.

After several substantial rest periods, man and broom had swept themselves up to me. I purposely ignored Marich as he now was working around my chair. Pretending not to see him, I speculated as to whether or not he was going to berate me because of the paper wads. As the broom came to a stop, Marich's voice came floating over my shoulders.

"You are new here," said the voice.

"I am," I answered, without glancing up.

After a short silence he said, "I don't like it when people throw papers on the floor."

Feigning ignorance, I asked "What kind of papers?" as I turned around.

"The ones under the table," he answered.

"Those have been there since yesterday," interjected Fat Joe, who was sitting on the opposite side of the table.

"Since yesterday?" said Marich in a studied and restrained manner. "If you say that they were there yesterday, you mean that I didn't sweep them out?"

"And you haven't swept them out today, either," laughed Skinny Joe.

Marich reacted to these words as if he had been splashed with boiling water. For several minutes he was speechless. When he finally regained command of himself, he blurted out, "You just be quiet! You don't give me my bread and, furthermore, you're not my boss."

"Ah, why argue! Skinny Joe is really glad he's not your boss and you, Marich, ought to be glad that your work is the most overpaid in America. Besides, both of you have a chance to become vice presidents of this enterprise. So why argue?" said Fat Joe as he secretly winked at his thin namesake.

Ascetic, by Milan Vojsk

Marich did not respond to these words, pretending that he had not heard them. He set about resuming his sweeping, but it already came to an end before it started.

Such conversations, which often became quarrelsome, took place daily. The paint shop crew could hardly wait to accommodate Marich and he, in turn, would not have fared so well without an argument with at least one employee every day.

Half an hour before lunch time, he propped his broom near the window, washed his hands and began to eat his lunch. When I turned toward the window again, he was no longer there. He had disappeared as completely as if the earth had swallowed him. If I hadn't gone to the bathroom, I would not have known what became of him. There he sat on a toilet seat with his pants up, as immobile as if cast in bronze. I felt certain that no noise, no racket could have awakened him from his noonday siesta.

At precisely two o'clock, Marich reappeared, pushing a wheelbarrow in which an empty barrel rattled. This container was intended to hold his hard-earned sweepings.

Before long, he was confiding details of his past life to me. For no reason he stepped up to me and, without any introduction, he said, "In the old country I was not a sweeper. There I had a better job." His emphasis on the words "better job" seemed to convey that in the old country he had been at least Minister of the Interior.

"What kind of work did you do?" I questioned.

"I was a musician."

"A musician!" I turned my face to hide my skeptical smile. "What kind of instrument did you play?"

"A bass viol."

Marich and I got along quite well. We probably never would have argued if I hadn't hung a for sale sign on his broom one day. This innocent prank upset him so, he would not even look at me for several days. This, too, was soon forgotten and in order to make peace with me, he gave me a good scolding because he had found dirt under my workbench.

It has been lonesome at the paint shop since Sweeper Marich reached the age of sixty-five and retired.

On the Saturday after New Year's, when I went to the Hungarian Garden, I received the surprise of my life. There was Marich with three gypsy musicians. He stood near the piano with his left hand raised somewhat as though he were holding someone by the neck while his right hand vigorously stroked a bass viol.

Louis Adamic (1899–1951), by Božidar Jakac

Louis Adamic

THE OLD ALIEN BY THE KITCHEN WINDOW

To his multitudinous family, relatives and friends, Anton Kmet is Oché Toné—*oché* meaning "father" or "old man" in his native Slovenian tongue, while Toné is the familiar abbreviation of his first name. He is an old man, no doubt about that.

His shrinking frame hunched over, his nape pushing down between his protruding, age-sharpened shoulder blades, and his legs crossed limply, Oché Toné sits all day long upon a hard, squeaky old chair by a small window in the kitchen on the ground floor of his house at 6208 Schade Avenue, in Cleveland, Ohio. He sits from ten to fourteen hours daily, and looks into the yard, in which there is nothing much to see; and, looking, he pulls at his corncob pipe and puffs with a slow, determined rhythm; and, sitting and looking at nothing much at all, and smoking, he thinks his thoughts.

Now and then he grunts or chuckles to himself as if to punctuate the things going through this head, or he lifts the large tremulous paw that rests on his thigh in a faint, vague gesture in the general direction of the cosmos, or he makes a remark to his wife or anyone who happens to come within the range of his voice, which is rather limited. Except for this and for the sucking and puffing at his pipe, he is perfectly still, often for hours at a spell. Sometimes he does not even smoke, but only sits and thinks, and frequently, no doubt, he just sits. He is in good health; only he is very old.

Within a period of three weeks during the late winter and early spring of 1940, sitting by the little four-pane window, Oché Toné celebrated six anniversaries—the eightieth of his birth in the village of Ajdovec, near the town of Zuzemberk, in Lower Carniola, then a province of Austria; the fiftieth of his arrival as an immigrant in the United States; the fiftieth, too, of his beginning to work for, and getting on the payroll of,

SOURCE: Louis Adamic, *From Many Lands* (New York and London: Harper and Brothers, 1940), 147-53, 162-64. Reprinted by permission of Harper & Row, Publishers, Inc.

The old alien, Tone Kmet, by Nancy Bukovnik, his granddaughter

the American Steel and Wire Company on Fortieth Street in Cleveland; the forty-eighth of his marriage to Karolina Novinec, who had come to America a year and a half after him from the village of Veliki Lipovec, also in Lower Carniola; the forty-seventh of the birth of the first of his eleven children, a son; and the twenty-fifth of his retirement on a monthly pension from his job, when he had decided that he had done his bit in the world and sat down in that chair (then new and free of squeaks) by the kitchen window, to gaze out and smoke and think from daybreak until nightfall every day of the week, week after week, month upon month, year in and year out; and to wait for his pension check, which the postman brings him once a month without fail.

As Oché Toné sees his life, now that it is tightly wrapped in old age, these anniversaries cover or suggest its high spots. Among them roam all his thoughts and talk. There is only one other important fact in his career, as he sees it: he is not a citizen of the United States, because he did not want to become one--a fact closely linked, however, to his notion that he is *neké vrsté Amerikanec vsé eno*, a kind of American, anyhow.

He understands some English but does not speak it. His medium of expression is a Slovenian peasant dialect, but he uses many American-English words twisted into Slovenian forms to fit his tongue. In his speech, for instance, a "house" is a *gauz*, "shoes" are *shukhi*, "street" is *shtrit*, and "beer" is *pir*.

He likes to tell "facts" about himself, which he has told so many times now that to him they are more true than truth itself; he has a surprisingly good memory, and each time he retells some of these "facts" he is more impressed by them than he was at the time of their occurrence. He is not hard to listen to, although, in common with most old people, he repeats himself a great deal. Off and on, when he catches himself repeating a bit of his life story in too close succession, he says something to this effect, "Eh, why not! I am like an old horse tethered to a pin in the ground, making the same steps all the time. At this stage of the game you don't go leaping into new adventures, so the old ones have to do."

His story, however, is not without significance, if that is the right word to attach to anything pertaining to an old man who has never been anything but a laborer. Perhaps I should say that parts of his story are typical of many aged immigrants who have been in America a long time without becoming citizens, and who are now dying at an increasing rate—albeit Oché Toné is apt to live to be a hundred. He wants to.

* * *

At thirty, on landing at Castle Garden in New York Harbor, Toné Kmet was what Slovenians call a *korenjak*, one who might be described as a "giant," or one constructed on a heroic scale. He was six foot three and all bone, blood, muscle, and hide; strong and straight as a pillar holding up the ceiling in a church, and not hard to look at otherwise. He had a shock of dark brown hair, an aquiline nose, an impressive mustache, and a bold, challenging look in his hazel eyes.

Kmet means "peasant" in Slovenian, and he was a peasant. He had no schooling but knew how to read a bit and to sign his name in an emergency. He had decided to come to the United States because he was his father's second son, and as such, along with all his younger brothers, obliged to leave the village and find a place and function for himself somewhere else. In the village of Ajdovec, a half-century ago, and before and since, things were tight and set economically, and only the oldest son was encouraged to remain at home. Fifty years ago, America was still a fairly new, though intensely interesting, idea in Carniola; but when Toné emigrated a score or more of Ajdovchani were already scattered through the various coal and steel and iron towns in the United States.

Toné Kmet had served for a number of years in the Emperor Franz Josef's army, and was none the worse for that experience. As a soldier, in fact, he had picked up a little German, which was useful to him in Cleveland, where a good many factory bosses were German immigrants from Austria and Germany.

From New York, Toné traveled in an immigrant train. At the depot in Cleveland, most of his fellow passengers were met by relatives or friends, but no one came for him. Not that he expected anyone. He had a slip of paper bearing the address of a number of the boys from the village of Ajdovec who had preceded him over; so he was not worried. But he was a bit bewildered by all the hubbub. His bundle over his shoulder, he stood outside the depot, watching the people jam themselves into the horse-drawn streetcars, and wondering which way to turn. Then a great dray loaded high with beer kegs drew up in front of him and the driver leaned downward from his lofty perch and yelled at him, "*Ti s' pa Kranjc, al' nis'?* You're a Carniolan, aren't you?" (Carniolan is usually synonymous with Slovenian.)

"*S'm,*" answered Toné. "I am."

Showing a broad grin, the driver invited him to hop on; he would take him wherever he was going. He also was a Slovenian immigrant, three years in America, and said he could always tell a *rojak* or fellow countryman on sight. "There's something about us!" He delivered beer to saloons in the Slovenian neighborhood and often picked up newcomers when he happened to pass by the depot.

He dropped Toné at Feliks Novinec's boardinghouse, where most of the other Ajdovchani lived. Feliks was the brother of Karolina, whom Toné married two years later, soon after she came over.

Two of the Ajdovchani at the house were employed in the American Steel and Wire Company's mill on Fortieth Street, and the morning after he arrived they took Toné Kmet along and told him to join the job-seeking crowd in the yard. Taller by a head than almost anyone else on the scene, he was among the first hired that morning, and assigned to a German straw boss, who put him to work with two other laborers. The job consisted of putting great bundles and coils of wire from a platform into freight cars.

Mochan kot hrast—strong as an oak, Toné Kmet tossed the coils and bundles as though they were trifles. The straw boss noticed this immediately and called the boss, who called the assistant plant superintendent, who called the chief superintendent, who decided that with Toné around the other two workers had nothing to do, and, indeed, were in his way; so he ordered them taken off the job and left Toné alone to do the work of three men. This, Toné continued to do with the greatest of ease; in fact, he thought the job was somewhat of a sinecure, and soon he received a higher wage—twelve cents an hour, while the other laborers were paid only ten.

He worked from ten to twelve hours daily, but not infrequently overtime stretched his workday to sixteen and occasionally even to eighteen hours. Sometimes his muscles creaked with fatigue when he took himself home, and he felt a little groggy, but thought he was doing all right, and America looked good to him.

* * *

Strong and good-looking, several years younger than he, Karolina Novinec caught Toné's eye, as she did the eyes of the other single boarders, immediately after she arrived from *stara kontra*, the old country. By-and-by, after he had made his intentions clear to her, she decided to marry him because he looked "steady."

Now, nearly half a century later, when he gets someone to listen to him, Oché Toné likes to tell of those days:

"To get married and start a home was no great stunt then. Sometimes I got only fifteen dollars on payday, which came every two weeks, but that wasn't bad. You managed on seven or eight dollars a week. If there was a lot of *obertaim*"—overtime—"and I brought home eighteen or twenty dollars, that was something to let the neighbors know about in some roundabout way so they could not accuse you of bragging, and they said, 'You're making good money, Toné; you and yours won't starve.'

"Living was cheap then. Naturally, when we got married, we had to furnish the flat. *Zlomka*, believe it or not, for thirty-five dollars we got everything we needed. Nowadays a young couple have to have four or five hundred dollars to set themselves up. Of course, our tastes then were not so high; we were satisfied with less than people are now: which may be good or bad, I don't know. But things really were cheaper then, in relation to wages. For three cents you got a quart of milk or a pound of meat. . . . Cleveland wasn't nearly as big a town then as it is now. Houses were thick only to about Fiftieth Street; there were a lot of farms within walking distance of

Memories, by Nancy Bukovnik

where most of the Slovenians lived, and you could get a four-hundred-pound hog for four dollars; then there was enough meat and lard to last the winter and well into spring, if you did not have too large a family or too many boarders. If you went into a butcher shop and bought a few pounds of pork or beef, you got free of charge all the tripe and lungs you wanted to take along; the butcher was glad to get rid of such stuff. . . . And any time of day you could step into a saloon, buy a glass of beer for a nickel, and eat your fill off the free-lunch counter. *Ya-ya*, this was a wonderful *kontra* then. . . .

"My wife and I rented a flat with two extra rooms; we put beds in them and took boarders, young fellows who were coming over from *stara kontra*: which helped. We were all content."

This last is one of his favorite sentences, with which he concludes most of his narrations about the old days. "We were all content." He rolls it off his lips with all the finality of a priest's "Amen."

* * *

For ten years Toné Kmet tossed the great bundles and coils of wire from the platform into the cars. Then he was promoted to a "better" job in the cooling department, where wire was treated in chemicals. The work here was much less strenuous and by now this, too, was all right with Toné Kmet. He had got to be forty and the heavy work on the platform had taken something out of him. Also, since the new job involved some responsibility, the pay was higher, "which didn't get me mad, either."

One day the chemists and several of the bosses were experimenting with a dangerous new chemical. They warned the men to be careful, and Toné heard and understood them all right. In a moment of bravado, however, meaning to impress the bosses, lest they should have forgotten that he was still a *korenjak* and that this work of handling these wire coils and bundles continued to be pretty much of a snap to him, he pushed a big bundle into the trough with his foot, as though he were kicking a lump of earth into a furrow. The iron platform on which he stood was wet; he slipped and, trying to regain his balance, lurched with one foot into the strong acid solution.

He was pulled out and his leg was quickly immersed in a vat containing another solution, supposed to counteract the first; but even so the leg was affected. A doctor treated him immediately, and he was taken home in an ambulance (a horse-drawn one, of course, for this occurred in 1901). He was laid up for several months. The doctor came to see him at first every two days, then once a week . . . "and I got my wages just as if I were working."

As already reported, when he was a young man, Toné's eyes held a bold, challenging look. They did later on, too. But that look was directed personally only at individuals who might want a fight or seek to vie with him, and to situations such as a great pile of wire bundles on the platform that had to be heaved into the cars by quitting time. By and large, it had no reference to institutions, such as governments or industrial mills or companies. Way down deep in him, peasant-like, Toné was a humble fellow in most respects; in fact, rather frightened, obedient, and "grateful"—grateful for the least demonstration of decency or generosity toward him. Or, at least, that was one fairly definite streak in his character (there were others). So, since his pay was nearly always a trifle higher than the other laborers', gratitude was always part of his feeling toward American Steel and Wire; and now, with all the good treatment he received following the accident, which he realized was entirely his own fault, he became clearly a "loyal employee," a "company man."

During the late 1900's and the early 1910's, there were a couple of strikes in the mill, but he never joined them. He felt miserable about this, especially since he knew he was called a scab, but he could not bring himself to go out. Eventually, too, his nonstriking became, to no small extent, a matter of policy between him and the company, for in 1910 American Steel and Wire entered into a pension plan under which the workers retired on partial pay after twenty-five years of continuous employment; and going on strike was interpreted by the company as an interruption of that continuity.

What helped to alleviate Toné Kmet's unhappiness during these strikes was that a good many of the men in the mill felt and acted as he did; and the strike leaders, as a rule, did not really expect or count on those who were working toward a pension to go out.

* * *

Like most peasant immigrants, in whom the property instinct was strong, Toné and Karolina Kmet aspired from the start to live in a dwelling of their own. To realize this on his laborer's wages was no easy matter, especially since a child was born to them on the average of every two years. But in 1907 they bought their first home, a small, cramped one-family house. Toné then acquired a couple of lots, mostly because everybody else he knew was plunging into real estate; and with Cleveland expanding at a great rate, he sold them in 1911 for three times the price he had paid for them. The following year he disposed of his house, or rather the corner on which it stood, for the building itself was worthless, and bought the substantial residence on Schade Avenue in which he now lives.

Karolina bore the eleven children, three boys and eight girls, during the first twenty years of their marriage. To say nothing of keeping up the payments on the house and lots, it was a problem to feed and clothe so large a family, for the cost of living, of course, did not stay at the 1893 level, when they married; yet all eleven children achieved adulthood and ten are still living and, in their various ways, doing as well as most Americans of the lower-middle or working class.

The oldest son, Anthony, Junior, commonly also known as Toné, started to work and contribute to the family income when he was but twelve. He served in the First World War, then trained himself to become a coremaker, and got a job with the United States Aluminum Company. He worked there until 1939, when in consequence of his war experience he suddenly died. He left a widow, who is a Slovenian immigrant, and two daughters and a son who are still in school.

The oldest daughter, Lina, was the first to marry. Her husband, Frank Turk, is a Slovenian born in Germany, where his parents had gone as emigrant laborers shortly before he was born. He was also trained to be a coremaker and works at that trade to this day. He and Lina, in their mid-forties, have eleven children, the youngest of whom is a few years old. Three of their daughters are married, and employed in the Richman Brothers' clothing factory, which is renowned for its satisfactory working conditions.

The second daughter, Mary, wed a grocer on St. Clair Avenue, which is the lifestream of the Slovenian section in Cleveland. The Depression hit him hard; when he was forced to sell either his home or his store, he sold the latter. Now he is a night watchman, while Mary cleans offices downtown. They have a boy and two girls, all grown up, two of them working.

Frances, the third daughter, was only sixteen when she married John Svete, a young fellow fresh from the old country. Also a coremaker, he too works for United States Aluminum, and Frances has been with General Electric now for fifteen years. They live in a house of their own and have three daughters, one of whom is married.

The fourth of the Kmet girls, Rose, married in 1935. Her husband, Janko Rogelj, an immigrant from Slovenia, is in the general insurance business and is an official of the South Slavonic Catholic Fraternal Union, secretary of the Slovenian gymnastic "Sokol" society, president of the Slovenian National Home on St. Clair Avenue, which is the center of the neighborhood's social and cultural life, and a writer of short stories and articles for the Slovenian language publications in the United States. The Rogeljs rent the upstairs part of the old folks' house, and have one child.

The fifth daughter, Tonca, or Antoinette, married in 1930. She has a boy and a girl. Her husband, John Bukovnik, is an immigrant who came over young and served as an aerial photographer in the First World War. Now he is a successful commercial photographer.

Vidé and Joe, the two boys born after Tonca, are single men, now in their late twenties, both coremakers with United States Aluminum, turning out airplane parts. They live with

New growth, by John A. Kapel

the old folks, as does their youngest sister, Gertrude, who, also unmarried, works at General Electric.

The other two daughters married American-born boys of Slovenian parentage. Mila works at Richman Brothers, while her husband is boss in a small factory. Bertha's man is an employee of the New York Central Railroad. Mila has no children. Bertha has a daughter.

Taking after the old man (for his wife is medium-sized), all the children are large people, as are almost all of the grown-up grandchildren, whose total now is twenty-four. And they are a handsome lot, both individually and together. Most of them resemble one another.

On Sundays and holidays the ground-floor apartment in the house on Schade Avenue, especially the kitchen, is full of the Kmet family, children and grandchildren. But they almost never come all at the same time. There is scarcely room for them.

American-born, all ten of the Kmet sons and daughters are, of course, American citizens; and having attended Cleveland's public schools, they speak fluent American English as it is usually spoken on their social level. But they know also their parents' Americanized peasant-Slovenian dialect, in which they occasionally kid and josh them for not being citizens.

* * *

The spring of 1939 was a hard period for Oché Toné. First, as already mentioned, his son Toné died. Then his Karolina, in her early seventies, went down with gallstones and had to undergo an operation, which put a pall on his lightheartedness for a while. In her absence he lost his appetite for *klobasé* and prunes and milk, but regained it with her return from the hospital. In a few months, she was her hardy old self again, taking charge of the Kmet household.

Oché Toné continues to take good care of himself, and barring accidents or serious illness, is apt to live for a long time yet. He is old, and looks it, but the core of his life is vital and healthy. His will to live is strong, but not intense; not such that its intensity might devour him. Life to him, when all is said and done, is a rather pleasant joke, and he sees himself deeply involved in it.

So he chuckles a great deal, and many of his remarks are touched with a dry, tongue-in-cheek humor. Some of his seemingly childish or naïve notions, attitudes and actions, including much of the ritual with the pension check, are really sly, indirect commentaries on his own amusing and essentially satisfactory existence; commentaries by which he is himself convinced. There is in him a bit of the artist, which is to be found in most Slovenian peasants. His sitting by the window is an act; he is an actor in a role he himself has created, and he goes on writing his own lines. He has the artist's eye for effect.

Now and then he requests his son-in-law upstairs to come down; he wants to ask or tell him something. His questions are roundabout, not neatly phrased, wandering in all directions, but seldom unclear or pointless after one gets on to the habit of his mind. They are hardly questions at all, but ramblings of an old mind with a streak of humor.

"Sit down, Janko," he said one day in connection with his several anniversaries early in 1940, "pull over a chair, come close here, so I don't have to talk so loud. . . . I've been thinking, Janko, about this office where my check comes from, this United States Steel and Carnegie Pension Fund. What is it? What kind of a place is it? . . . Well," answering his own question, as is his wont, "I imagine it's an office in some great building, high up near the clouds, with desk and writing machines and water coolers, like the office of the American Steel and Wire mill, which I saw a few times. And there they sit, whoever they are; they sit by their desks and writing machines, and make out checks and sign them, and then they send them out—like gods in heaven. And what I want to know, Janko, is this: what am I to them? Am I just a name, someone on their list of names? For twenty-five years nobody has come to see me. No questions are asked. They must be *vsevedni*"—omniscient—"or how do they know I am still around? They must be gods; no?"

He chuckled.

"Besides, where do they get the money to send me? Do they ever say to themselves: when is that old buzzard on Schade Avenue in Cleveland going to die, so we can stop sending him money? Here I am. For twenty-five years they've been sending me $21.40 a month. That's a lot of coin. Where do they get it? They must be gods, *vsemogochni*"—omnipotent. "Their checks are good. There hasn't been a bad one yet. . . . Of course, Janko, another explanation may be that they are just Americans. Smart people, these *Amerikanci*"—chuckling again.

"But jesting aside, Janko," he went on, "wouldn't you think that they would get tired paying me all this money, with me sitting here, not doing anything, getting calluses in the wrong place, just sitting; or that they would run out of money, even if they are Americans? Not that I worry about them. It's their business. I did my bit. . . .

"And you know what, Janko: something else has occurred to me. Maybe those strikers were right. Maybe the American Steel and Wire didn't pay us enough for our work, not even me, although my wage was always a little higher than the others'. Maybe I did work too hard, crowded my years together too fast with *obertaim* and doing two or three men's work, and it may be that now I'm getting only what was my due all along because I worked in that mill for twenty-five years. Of course, it may be that they did not figure I would live so long and get the best of them in the deal. Maybe I'm getting more than my due.

If so, the joke is on them; eh, Janko? The whole thing is funny, if you come to think of it. Me getting a pension! It's a joke; but maybe only to me. So I want to live a long time yet. I enjoy it so. What are jokes for but to be enjoyed; and if I die, who would enjoy this one?"

* * *

On one of my visits I mentioned to Oché Toné that there were people in the United States, including members of Congress in Washington, who were disturbed about the aliens and noncitizens, and that some wanted to deport all the foreign-born who did not have their naturalization papers, while others wished to pass laws requiring all noncitizens to register and be fingerprinted.

"*Taku?*—So?" said the old alien by the kitchen window. He was silent for a few minutes, smoking, looking out of the window. Then he chuckled and said, "Papers, papers! God gave the fish freedom in the sea and lakes and rivers, and birds all over the earth, but from a man somebody always wants some kind of paper." He smiled, shaking his head. "But, *nu*, maybe I was wrong in not taking out the citizenship papers; mind you, I don't say I was; I just say maybe I was. Let me tell you, though, what you do: you bring those people here on the first of the month, any month, whoever they are; you bring them and I'll show them my American paper, which says that I worked all right and did what was expected of me. I didn't ask for this paper. I didn't pay for it; Bostijancich, or Boston, didn't have to use his pull to get it for me. I worked until I did enough for one man's lifetime, and America has been giving me this paper once a month now for twenty-five years. . . . You tell those people, whoever they are, to come to my house and I'll show them. . . . But, of course, if they want me to get registered and—what do you call it?—fingerprinted, if that will make them feel better, I'll be glad to oblige, even if I have to go out of the house to do it. . . ."

He fell silent again, sitting and pulling on his pipe, and looking out into the yard, where a sparrow sat on a limb of a tree close to the window. Then Oché Toné chuckled again, "Look at him! They call him an American sparrow; what makes him American? Has he got his papers? Is he registered? Listen: back in Ajdovec, in lower Carniola, I saw sparrows which were no different." The chuckle broke forth again with real gaiety. Then: "A sparrow is a sparrow, a man is a man, *al' ne'* —isn't that so?"

Karel Mauser (1918–1977), by France Gorše

Karel Mauser

JOHN KOVACH

Translated by Joseph Zelle

He waited till the alarm clock finished ringing. Then, while still in bed, he pressed down on his legs, stretched himself, let out a sigh just as he did every morning, and sat up.

How quickly the night passes, he thought.

As his legs touched the floor, he felt for his slippers, put them on, and walked to the window. It was quite light already. Enough daylight had filtered through the smoke and fog so that he could well distinguish the three tall poplars protruding through the grayness with their short, dense branches.

His eyes stopped at the old, dilapidated garage. At the time he had bought the house, the garage had still been in good condition, even if the wood cried out for paint. The years and the oversaturated air had deteriorated it completely. It was still standing, but the rotted boards sagged in all directions, and it always seemed to him that the first strong wind would topple over the rottenness in a heap. The loss would not be great. People had begun to desert this place shortly after the factory had moved away. The people had left; he had stayed on. As fed up as he was with the weeds behind the poplars and with the long, brown grass, he still did not want to move.

He had bought the house soon after getting married. Three children had been born behind those wooden walls: Louis, Steve and Agnes. Louis was in Akron now, married; Steve had moved away to Euclid and had been married there; and Agnes, grieving for her mother, had married and left with her husband for Florida.

He had been without a wife for a long time now. She had died so unexpectedly. On the street—a car had knocked her down. After that, she had tossed about in the hospital for two weeks, and then she was gone forever.

SOURCE: Karel Mauser, "John Kovach," *Meddobje*, vol 2, nos. 4-5, 1956, 197-99.

Multi-position piece, by Stanko Tušek

Almost every day, as he glanced out the window, he would think like this, spit down below into the garden, and decide to retire. But then he would dress anyway, put the coffee on, wash, make a couple of sandwiches, and after the coffee was brewed, pour a little milk, and sit down to breakfast. He could not poke around too long. He had to take a bus to Public Square and there transfer to the St. Clair bus. And that standing around and waiting sometimes took up to a quarter of an hour. At seven he was already punching the button on the machine.

He knew that he would not retire. He could not. He was used to the work, and if he thought it over, what in the world would he do all the day long in the house? Louis came home only once a year for a visit, Steve perhaps three times, and Agnes barely once every two years. They wrote cards for the holidays. That was all. Little did they think of his loneliness. Well, he didn't count on their company anyway. He had known that they would scatter. If she were still alive, so that home would really be home, perhaps one of them would still drop in, if for no other reason than baby-sitting.

Thus he went quietly to the bus every morning. Before entering, he would shove a lump of chewing tobacco in his mouth with three fingers. He had learned that at the factory.

Once in the shop, he always felt better. Everything smelled of oil. The machines waited neatly in order, the lights were lit, and there were even nice golden teardrops of oil on the bulbs. As the bell rang, he would push the button. With a strange trembling, the grinding wheel would start up, sound like neighing, and as it reached full speed, it would grumble along amiably. He would stick a rag in his pants' rear pocket for wiping his hands and look over the work. Three long drills. A special order! He would take one of the drills in his hand and twirl it. He would study the order, examine the tolerance, the special instructions. What time-consuming work!

John was a good grinder. All his life, he enjoyed his work, but something had been troubling him for a good four months. His hands were beginning to tremble. The week before, because of his trembling fingers, he had bumped a drill against the grindstone and there had been a hundred dollars' damage. He was called into the office and the boss had glanced at him good-naturedly from head to toe.

"We're getting old, eh, John?"

He was grinning as he showed him the ruined drill. It was a good thousandth under size at the injured place. Useless!

"Tough luck," John smiled derisively to himself. However, everything within him was crying. He dreaded the time when someone would say to him, "We're getting old, eh, John?" He did not want to hear those words; it was as if they already meant death, a coffin lined with silk, and everything that went with it.

Old man, by Steven A. Rebeck

For four months now he had been struggling to steady his fingers. Secretly, he would bend them and try to hold them out straight, gritting his teeth all the while. Sometimes, it seemed to him that his fingers shook no longer, that they were perfectly steady, just as when he had first come to the machine. Then he would see in horror that his little finger was shaking, that the third finger was shaking, that all the fingers were shaking. It seemed as if on purpose, to mock him, just as the boss had, "We're getting old, eh, John?"

Sometimes he would bring the drill near the grindstone three times, four times, to catch the points of the centers in the little holes. It would not work. His fingers were trembling, his whole hand was trembling, and John felt heavy drops on his forehead. He would lay the drill back on the bench and wipe his brow with the rag.

After that he would manage to catch the drill in the center. The wheel would approach the steel, the grindstone slowly lick the rotating piece, and a great joy would overtake him, as he would see the rough upper layer disappearing, the steel beginning to shine, just the way it had to be.

Today he was in a good mood. The machine, which sometimes had its whims, was running smoothly. Two drills were already finished. He wiped them with his rag and measured each one three times. Taper, tolerance, everything was right, just as specified in the order. Now the grindstone was lapping at the last piece. John quietly whistled to himself and wiped his hands with the rag. It was three o'clock. One more hour.

He took out the piece from the centers and measured it. Still two thousandths too thick. He started putting it back. "Damn it!" His hand was trembling like a branch right up to his shoulder. Stubbornly he tried, even though something kept telling him to lay the drill on the bench and wait.

"I'm not old; I can do it, just as these youngsters can. I'll show them; I'll show the boss, too."

There was a screech, a long black streak etched the smooth steel, and John's eyes grew misty.

He held the drill in his trembling hands, kept twirling it, and the deep black stain hissed back at him like a viper's head: "You see me, you see me?"

His neighbor at a machine nearby came to him and shook his head oddly.

"Son-of-gun! And over two inches thick!"

He did not hear him. He raised his head and looked towards the office. The boss was quietly sitting by the window writing something.

He gripped the drill in his hand and slowly went between the machines. It seemed to him that the drill was unbearably heavy, that just about everything he had was contained in it, even those three poplars and those weeds, that coffin lined in

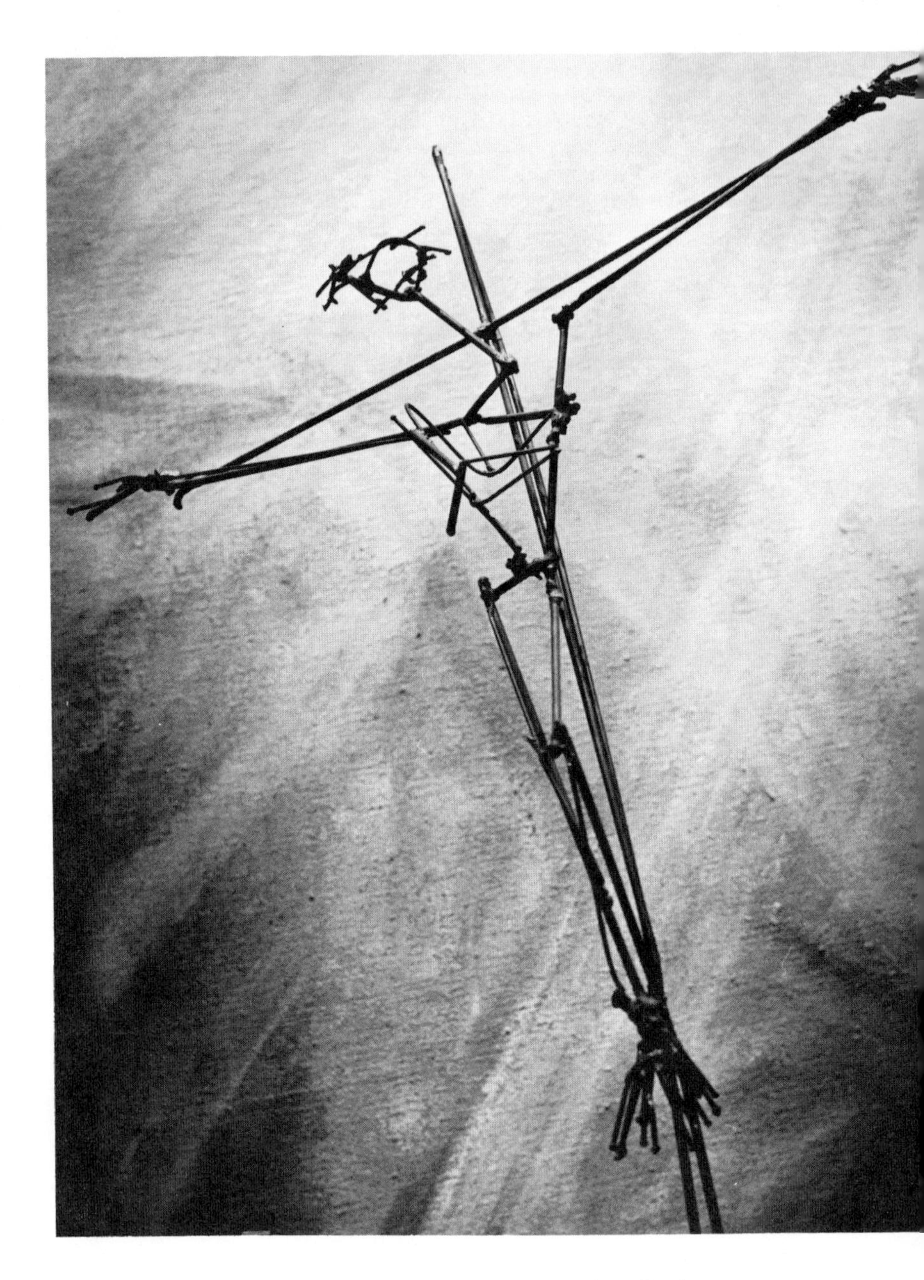

Christ on the cross, by Lillian Brulc

silk, and that last trip, when you are laid on a cart before the altar steps, where you get the last blessing.

The boss with half-closed eyes twirled the drill in his hand. He was not laughing.

"I'll ask, John," he said coldly. He did not look up at him.

Three days after that he was transferred to another machine. For children! He was given a chair, and with a little conical grinding stone, he smoothed the holes that were rough.

He looked about and, with a peculiar troubled look, stopped at his old machine. A strong, young lad was standing behind it. He had been like that once. This one's hands did not tremble at all; with a grin he placed a drill between the centers.

"This will be easy work, John," he heard the boss say.

He just nodded his head and sat down.

The motor was running evenly, the stone was rotating quietly. It seemed to John that he was sitting on a target, that everybody was looking at him, that all of them were going to the office to examine his latest drill with the deep black stain.

As soon as he got home, he lay down and did not even warm up the coffee. In the morning, too, he did not step to the window as usual.

Old!

And then came that afternoon. He had eaten his lunch as always on the chair beside the machine. He felt strangely tired, felt a tightness in his head. He leaned against the machine, his back propped up against an iron container alongside.

When the bell rang, he did not budge. He did not push the button, did not straighten up, did not look at the clock as he usually did.

"John!" his neighbor called to him. "Kovach!"

He did not answer.

The young man from the other side gave him a push on the shoulder. He moved only slightly, but did not get up. The young man knelt down to see John's face.

Blood was slowly trickling from John's nostrils.

"Stroke," someone said hollowly.

Then came the stretchers. Someone wiped off the clotted blood on John's machine. Someone also turned off the light.

Each and all of us, by France Gorše

III

ALL KINDS OF PEOPLE

Sister Lavoslava Turk

Sister Lavoslava Turk

MY LITTLE ANGELS

I shall always cherish fond memories of my first American pupils. The siege of the fortress of my heart began when I first entered the classroom. Soon the little ones had won it over completely. Even now, after so many years, I love to think of them and I include them in my prayers.

I felt that all my pupils were "little angels." Doesn't every mother consider her child to be the most beautiful, the most talented, almost a genius? Frequently, I would discuss my pupils with Sister Lea. She, too, taught only "little lambs" who sometimes became regular "rams." How we laughed when we told of our successes in breaking the horns of this or that one as soon as they had sprouted!

My feelings were terribly hurt whenever any Sister complained about my "little angels." But I could not defend them, for I realized that Sister was right. They prepared many a bitter hour for me, but these were soon forgotten, for on the scales children's innocence, obedience, simplicity, and other beautiful virtues weighed so much heavier.

Lives there a king so respected, admired, loved, and adored by his subjects as a Sister-teacher who is loved by her pupils? She is a queen—the queen of little hearts. Whatever she says is law, even in their homes: "Sister said so!"—and there can be no higher court.

What a beautiful opportunity a Sister has for molding children's hearts, for sowing seeds of goodness that will ripen into a rich harvest later!

How I wish that I were a poet so I could sing a canticle about our beautiful and exalted vocation—and about my "little angels!"

SOURCE: M. Lavoslava Turk, *Pesem šolske sestre* (Celovec: Družba Sv. Mohorja, 1974), 79.

Frank Mlakar (1913–1967)

Frank Mlakar

OSIP BUYS A HOME IN CHICKEN VILLAGE

Osip dared not admit even to himself that he was looking for a suitable house to buy. Lenka and he had managed to save a fair amount from their wages, but the sum was insufficient for even a down payment on a house. Nevertheless, he wandered the streets of the Chicken Village, dreaming to himself.

The few blocks of "bordingauses" and saloons surrounding St. Lizaveta's had once comprised the whole of the Chicken Village. An evening's stroll would have covered the area. In those days there were fields of weeds and grass among the factories, mills, tenements, and wooden frame dwellings. Now all the fields had been built on. Dwellings occupied all the narrow spaces that might have shown a patch of bare earth. Then there was nothing to do but move out in other directions. To the north, the lake stopped the movement; to the west, the blocks of mills. The south was cut off by President Avenue and its streetcar line. But not for long. A sudden convulsion, and the Slovenian colony had spilled itself over the dividing line. Slovenian names commenced to appear above the shops. A new tongue was heard on the sidewalks.

The people pushed east, past Kittman Street, Champion Street, Eldorado, Promenade, as far as Manager Street. Could another narrow house be crowded in here somewhere?

It took Osip several weeks to explore all the streets of the Chicken Village, and always his walks were bounded by the mills in one direction, the lake in another, President Avenue in the south and by Manager Street in the east. As soon as he moved out of this territory, it seemed to him that the streets were less clean, the houses not so sturdy, or that people sitting on the porches gave him a hostile stare as he passed by.

Now and then he was recognized by a worker from the mill and invited in for a drink and a chat. Inside the man's house

---

SOURCE: Frank Mlakar, *He, the Father* (New York: Harper and Brothers, 1950), 62-72. Reprinted by permission of Harper & Row, Publishers, Inc.

Chicken shack, by Nancy Bukovnik

he would look about him, exclaiming at the number of rooms and their bigness, the fancy furniture—thinking to himself as he said these things that his own place would be even bigger and better.

One evening late that autumn, Osip began his explorations with an air of keen expectation. A friend had told him of an unusual house on Promenade Street that was for sale.

Overhead a yellow moon sailed lazily. He almost ran along the sidewalks, smiling at his eagerness to believe what he had been told. He went past the big "bordingauses," past a group of children who were chattering among themselves in American. One of them, with his face turned to a pole, was calling off a string of numbers. The others went fleeing for their lives in all directions. Osip saw them hiding themselves, in the shadows, in cavelike doorways, behind a solitary tree that had lost its leaves and was cowering in two feet of dirt between sidewalk and street.

He hurried on. At Promenade Street he came to a stop. To the north lay the railroad tracks, gleaming in the moonlight like ribbons. Somewhere in the opposite direction lay the house he was seeking. Was it likely to be the kind of house he wanted? Most of the habitations in this neighborhood were terribly old, deserted by the Americans a long time ago.

Behind him, four blocks back, lay the wire mills, but here it was another world altogether. In the moonlight he could see the twin rows of narrow dwellings. Not a factory chimney anywhere, not a saloon. There were lights shining in some of the houses. Everything was quiet, peaceful.

He turned into the street. The house was located midway down the block. The first quick glance told him what he wanted to know. It was the house he had been looking for. He had walked up and down this street a dozen times; how could he have overlooked it? In his mind it was his already. It had been waiting there for him, so that he should come on it at just this moment, when he was ready for it.

In Osip's eyes the straight, clean, and almost gaunt lines of the house were proof of the good craftsmanship that had gone into it. It was solidly constructed, resting securely on stone piers. A properly steep roof covered it. All the proportions of length and width and height were so finely adjusted that they could not have been altered without making it a different and inferior sort of house.

He exulted in its simple beauty. His heart went out to the person who had made it.

"He knew what he wanted and didn't trust others to make it for him," exactly, as he, being Osip Princevich and not someone else, had known from the start that he could not buy the kind of cradle he wanted for his firstborn and would have to make it himself.

Landscape composition, by H. Gregory Prusheck (Perušek)

The dwelling had once been a farmhouse, with land running down to the lake. Over the decades other houses had crept up to its walls. The acres of land had dwindled to the few feet of dirt surrounding it. The fields on which the forgotten American farmer had grown his crops were now covered by mills in which machines pounded and thundered, and by myriad houses whose inhabitants spoke a language that was not American. This little core of an old vanished life stood alone and lost in the disfigured landscape.

Its suggestion of oldness appealed to Osip. As he went up to it, he could see even in the moonlight that a crime had been committed on the venerable thing. Its boards were unpainted and cracked. Nails showed their heads. The fence sagged inward. The sidewalk leading to the porch was broken; grass grew up from it. But these imperfections pleased him. He would have been disappointed to find the house perfect. Now he himself would bring it back to its rightful beauty. The sagging shutters on the windows, the curlicues of wood tacked on to the eaves, the trellises on the porch—all would be removed, the simplicity restored.

With his heart in his throat, Osip went to the door and knocked.

After a while he heard slow and halting steps. As the door swung open, Osip saw an old man, bent almost double, his face cracked with a hundred seams, his thin shoulders covered by a blanket.

"Yanez Anzlovar?"

"Come in." The old man turned and led the way to the round-bellied stove, which was cherry red with heat. Here he let himself down slowly into a black rocking chair and motioned Osip to take a place near him.

Osip sat down, wondering at the old man's wastefulness in having a fire on what was a comparatively warm autumn night.

Yanez Anzlovar noticed his expression and said, "I'm cold all the time. I can't get warm." His voice was pitched low. Osip had to lean forward to hear him.

"Are you here about the house?" He was surveying Osip from under his white brows.

"Yes."

The old man began to rock himself slowly, tapping his slippered toes into the floor like a child engrossed by rhythmic motion.

"It's a good house, but it hasn't brought me any luck," he said. "Once I thought it would stay mine until I died and then go to my children."

Osip could not repress a start as he heard these words. But Yanez Anzlovar was absorbed in his own thoughts and went on with, "Some of my kids were born on the other side, some here. Now I've got no one. My old lady died two years ago."

A clock ticked loudly on the shabby dresser. The rug on the floor was threadbare. From the molding that ran round the walls a few pictures were hung: one was of Christ; another showed a young woman clad in a voluminous white garment, her hair piled in coils on her head. The third picture was of a young man whose chin was supported by an incredibly tall and stiff collar.

"That's me, when I came here forty years ago, long before Smrekar and his saintly crew." A spark of life crept back into one faded watery eye; the other remained closed. "The Christ was the old lady's. I let it stay there because she liked it."

Yanez Anzlovar was picking at the blanket on his shoulders with his transparent fingers, trying to settle it more comfortably. Osip helped him. He felt there was something queer about this old man who appeared interested not so much in selling his house as in finding someone to listen to him. "What have I walked into?" he wondered. "Is he sincere about selling the house?" His first words had not been the sort to please a prospective buyer.

"There wasn't a Slovenian here then," continued the garrulous ancient. "Only Germans and Jews, Polacks and Americans. I went years without saying a word to the neighbors. Then the kids grew up and I learned some American." The chair creaked as he tipped himself forward and backward.

"My children thought I knew more than I did, and so they spoke American to me all the time. I was ashamed to confess that I didn't understand them. I told myself that I would learn the language some day, but it was too late and I never did. One by one they deserted the nest, until only the little one was left of seven. Then she, too, married, and the old lady and I were left alone, just as if we had never had any children at all. The house became as quiet as a grave. The old lady died one day, and I was alone. Now I've decided to go back to the old country. They can bury me in the place where I was born."

A spasm of coughing shook him. The blanket slipped from his shoulders. He blew his seamed cheeks in and out fiercely, trying to catch his breath.

"Can I help you?" asked Osip, bewildered by the unreal, dreamlike turn the interview had taken.

The old man's fingers on the black arms of the rocking chair were quivering like aspen leaves. After a while he began again, his voice unwinding itself from the recesses in which it had been stored.

"I'm worn out," he said. "They gave me the pension too late. What can I do with it now? I've told the man from the mill to bring it to me in dollar bills. I throw them into the air and let them fall at my feet. Then I sit here and look at them and say to myself, 'Well, Yanez Anzlovar, you're an old fool, all right. This is all it's brought you. There's your life on the floor. There's the blue right eye you lost in the mill. There's your old wife who never had any fun. There are your lost American children. Everything's passed you by. You'll die soon without knowing why you were put on earth.' Now there's only the money left. That's why I sometimes spit on it, to show myself that man is better than a bit of paper."

Osip put in timidly, "About the house, is it really for sale?"

"See if you want it first. Of course it's for sale. What am I to do with it?"

He was still going on when Osip left him to explore the house. As he passed from room to room his elation mounted. He saw that the floors everywhere were solid to his tread, though they were hollowed with wear near the doorways. Board joined board with a true edge. Here and there the square head of a handmade nail showed itself. There were probably hundreds of such nails hidden from the eye, all handmade, of iron patiently heated and pounded into shape, all wrought with the same careful craftsmanship.

Osip walked through rooms in which no one had lived for a long time, saying to himself, "I don't have to see any more. It's mine already, every bit of it. This house has been waiting for me, no matter what the old man says about it being unlucky. His life is finished; mine is beginning."

But he could not stop looking. He went into each of the seven rooms once again. He went into the windowless cellar where the long-dead farmer had stored his apples. The beams that supported the weight of the house had been hewn from living timber and still showed the marks of the ax.

Yanez Anzlovar was drowsing when Osip came back to him. His mouth had fallen open, revealing a few blackened stumps of teeth. He wakened at Osip's touch.

"How much—about how much would it be?" stammered Osip.

"Three thousand dollars. In cash. I won't live long enough to collect a mortgage. I'm taking the money with me to the old country. Is it yes or no?"

Three thousand dollars. Where would he get that amount of money?

"Yes," he heard himself whispering, "the answer is yes. I will be back tomorrow night."

"Well, then, shake hands on it," said Yanez Anzlovar. "In cash."

"Yes, yes. Tomorrow."

Osip stumbled out of the house.

Three thousand dollars. He was making twenty-two dollars a week, Lenka another nine. Sixteen hundred and twelve dollars a year in all.

Did he sleep at all that night? He remembered something that was either a dream or else part of his half-wakeful imaginings. He had seen the hut again, the same hut that once figured so prominently in his dreams. But this time the hut was not torn down by winds. He saw it take fire and burn to ashes. In the midst of the leaping flames he glimpsed quite clearly the figure of an old man slowly rocking himself on a black chair, serenely oblivious to the fire around him, until he was abruptly swallowed and lost to sight.

Osip was aware of an intense anxiety the moment he opened his eyes. The house on Promenade Street! The dream of the hut meant that something had happened to ruin his chances of getting Yanez Anzlovar's house.

"It's too early to get up," said Lenka drowsily, hearing him move. "Did the clock ring?"

He decided he would tell her nothing yet. "Go back to sleep. The light must have wakened me. See, the sun's beginning to rise."

Lenka obediently turned her back to the window and was soon asleep again.

It was while he was sitting at breakfast that Osip thought of Smrekar. The saloonkeeper was fond enough of Lenka that he would listen sympathetically to anything that might affect her happiness. He owned this building and was reputed to have title to several other important properties in the Chicken Village; he was undoubtedly the only person Osip knew who might have three thousand dollars available in cash. Osip pushed the breakfast aside and hurried out.

Downstairs Smrekar was talking to a man in a leather apron. Outside the saloon a pair of horses stared gloomily at the pavements. The morning was gray, the sun cold. The man in the leather apron came out, climbed up to his seat on the beer wagon, and set the horses in motion.

"What will it be, Osip?" said Smrekar, eying him with curiosity. "This is the first time I've seen you here in the morning."

"Nothing to drink, *Gospodar*."

"Is Lenka all right? There's no trouble?"

"Lenka's sleeping. I came to see you about something."

"So?"

"*Gospodar* Smrekar, I want you to help me buy a house."

He blurted it out all in one breath, despite the decision he had made to go at the business calmly. Ignoring Smrekar's startled expression, he began rapidly to describe the property on Promenade Street, the amount of money he needed to effect the sale.

With a wry grin Smrekar took in the situation.

"And so you come to me?"

"I've no one else to turn to. *Gospodar* Smrekar, I'd do anything to get that house, give you whatever you want for the use of your money."

"Can't you get a loan from the Slovenian bank?"

"Lenka and I have only a couple hundred dollars. They wouldn't give me a mortgage on that. I've no security but my word."

"They're businessmen," said Smrekar, "Slovenians who have become American businessmen. They learned quickly. Tell me something, Osip. Did Lenka put you up to asking me?"

"It was my idea, *Gospodar* Smrekar. Lenka knows nothing about the house yet."

"You haven't told her!"

"I wished it to be a surprise. I wanted to make all the arrangements, then lay the title to the house in her hands." And now, as he spoke these words, he felt a momentary pang of doubt. Should he have approached Smrekar without speaking to Lenka first?

A smile wreathed the saloonkeeper's face. "So that's how it is. Don't you know that Lenka doesn't want to live in the Chicken Village?"

"Excuse me, *Gospodar*," and he rushed on, scenting Smrekar's interest, "she's impatient and restless now only because we don't have a place of our own, because we live in a single room. No offense meant, *Gospodar* Smrekar, but that's how it is. We can't live in one room much longer. We want children, space for them to live in."

"I will tell you what," said Smrekar casually, an impish grin playing across his pink features; "go to work now. There's no reason for you to lose a day's pay. Let me see what can be done. I'll go to old Yanez myself. If the place is worth the money, perhaps something can be arranged. I promise nothing yet, but . . . well, let's say the mortgage would rest in my hands, to be paid off properly, just as you'd pay it at the bank. I'll be doing this not for any sentimental reasons, or because of Lenka, as you may be thinking, but as business, a good six-percent business."

Osip gawked at these words. It wasn't possible that the matter could be settled this easy. There was a trick in it somewhere. What did Smrekar's queer grin mean? He had half a mind to back out of the deal. Then everything was washed away in a flood of joy, and he had caught up the saloonkeeper's hand. If he hadn't been ashamed to, he would have fallen to his knees in gratitude.

"Off with you now," said Smrekar jovially, as though he were hugely pleased at some private joke.

In the ensuing days Osip put his name to the documents that Smrekar several times laid down for him to sign. The saloonkeeper seemed animated by an eagerness equal to Osip's, but the young man no longer wondered about it. Each signature brought him that much closer to the dreamed-of property. He dared not go to the house again for fear he might upset the luck that was so extraordinarily favoring him.

Light and shadows (baptistry in Panama), by Lillian Brulc

Lenka did not fail to notice his preoccupation or the laughter he spilled affectionately over her. "You'll know everything soon," he promised when she pressed him.

"You're not doing something you shouldn't?"

"Of course not! What a notion."

A frown settled itself on Lenka's face. What could he be planning? He seemed a different man. It was strange that he would not confide in her, take her into his confidence.

And then one evening Smrekar beckoned Osip into the little room he used as an office. In his hand he held a document of some sort. Osip followed him at once.

"There it is," said Smrekar simply, "the deed to the house. Anzlovar intends to be out of the place next week. He's going to the old country to spend his last years. All his furniture goes with the house. It's written down here. He's expecting you tonight."

Osip was inarticulate with gratitude.

"Pay what you owe me, and there'll be no complaints," said Smrekar. "You're young, so it shouldn't take you long to square the whole debt. Find Lenka now. She's got my permission to leave."

Now that everything had turned out the way he had hoped it would, Osip could not believe it. The saloonkeeper finally pushed him out of the office and, seeing Lenka watching them, gave her an imperious nod that brought her running.

"What's wrong?" she exclaimed.

"Nothing's wrong," said Smrekar. "You two are seeing a friend for me. Take off your apron and leave. Osip will tell you what there's to know." He returned to his stool behind the bar and waved to them as they left.

"What is it, Osip?" asked Lenka, once they were out on the street. "Who is this friend? Why are we seeing him?"

He smiled down at her. "You'll know, you'll know. . . ."

On Promenade Street he led her to a lighted house. He climbed the porch stairs and knocked loudly on the door.

"Whose house is this?"

He knocked again. When there was still no answer, he said, "It's our house. We may as well go in. We've come here to take possession."

Lenka seemed to wilt as she took in the meaning of his words. Her hand went to her mouth.

Osip pushed open the door.

Yanez Anzlovar was sitting quietly in his rocking chair. One blue eye was staring; the other, as always, was closed. Scattered on the floor were the dollars Smrekar had paid him for the house. He was grinning down at them.

The old man was dead.

Kazimir Zakrajšek, O.F.M. (1878–1958)

Kazimir Zakrajsek, O.F.M.

A FATHER'S LOVE

Translated by Edward Krasovich

It was at the time of a big strike in Chicago a number of years ago. For weeks already, workers had been walking the streets and hoping for a settlement of the labor dispute.

Jacob Cvek was one of the men working at the mill who had walked off his job with the others. He believed in labor unions.

It was with heavy heart that he walked home from the mill, on the last day of his employment, taking his paycheck to his wife. There was a bill at the grocer's, a bill at the butcher's, and they owed the milkman. Johnny needed shoes, and Annie needed a dress. If his paycheck were four times what it was, it still would not be enough to cover the bare necessities they needed. Now he was without work! And God knows how long the strike would last.

So Jacob was a sad man when he came home and with some trepidation broke the news about the strike to his wife. She was shocked. She had been in poor health since her last childbirth. Now what if she should become bedridden?

That's how things were at the time of that strike. Week after week the labor negotiations dragged on, but it seemed that no agreement could be reached.

Hunger began to be felt at the Cvek household. Jacob was able to find a part-time job occasionally, but that helped very little. Hunger and sorrow overcame his wife, who was now completely ill and bedridden.

It was very difficult for the man of the house when he reflected on the poverty and misfortune that had befallen his family. If only he could find a job so that he could at least provide his wife and children with the necessities of life! Every morning he went from factory to factory seeking employment, with no results.

SOURCE: K[azimir Zakrajšek], "Očetova ljubezen," *Ave Maria Koledar*, 1920, 86.

On strike, by Ted Kramolc

One morning, cold and hungry, he walked from one factory to another. It was bitter cold. He came to the employment office of a factory where there was a long line of applicants seeking employment. As he stood at the end of this line, he picked up a discarded newspaper. Leafing through it, he read:

"Wealthy N. N. lies fatally ill at X Hospital. Only a transfusion of a rare type of blood from strong and healthy individuals can save his life. Acceptable donors will be paid handsomely."

As he read this notice he wondered whether his blood would be acceptable. "I'm strong and healthy," he thought.

"We are not hiring any more men today. We'll take on a few more tomorrow morning," the clerk announced to those standing in line.

As the men dispersed, Jacob thought, "Now I have no other choice but to go find out about my blood." And he hurried over to the hospital.

The doctor gave him a thorough examination. "You have the proper type blood and you are healthy enough," said the doctor. "Your blood will be acceptable!"

Jacob's blood was drawn, and he received his fee.

With great joy and happiness Jacob brought home groceries and other necessities for his family.

"Where on earth did you get the money?" asked his wife.

"It's best, dear, that you do not know."

"You're certainly not going to keep secrets from your wife," she said.

Jacob kept the news from her as long as he could. Finally, reluctantly, he told her what had happened.

"You bought us bread with your blood?"

"Yes, dear. I could no longer stand seeing your hunger," he said as the happy little children embraced their good father.

Jim Debevec

Jim Debevec

THE HOLIEST THING ALIVE

Probably the most unselfish person in the world is a Slovenian mother! Her children always come first.

She may have come from the old country (Slovenia, Yugoslavia). Mother there was accustomed to the hard life and taught her daughter the principles of thrift, religious devotion, and difficult physical toil as a means of obtaining satisfaction in this life.

In the old country, the mother often worked in the fields beside her husband. It was not uncommon to see her chopping the firewood, or bringing in the well water.

In this country the Slovenian mother followed her mother's pattern. The newly arrived citizen could be seen working in factories, helping as a domestic, and in rural districts, helping the husband with the daily farm burdens.

She is thrifty. If family obligations at home prevent her from seeking employment outside the domicile, she can find a million ways to save money in her own environment.

As an example, she never buys frozen foods; she would rather spend all day Sunday cooking *zinkrofi* (filled dough). She prefers homemade soup to the store-bought variety. "Open up a can of soup? What's that?" she might ask. Nobody can bake *potica* (nut roll) as well as she.

She spends a good deal of her time jarring foods for later use.

When shopping for clothes, the Slovenian mother is constantly thinking of her family. She usually buys for the entire household, forgetting (on purpose) her own needs. "I can do without. You must face the public" is her reasoning.

Often she is in charge of the family finances. She always saves some money for the future. That usually means buying a home. If the husband brings home fifty, or a hundred, or two hundred dollars a week, at least ten percent of it will go into the bank.

SOURCE: *The Euclid News-Journal*, 11 May 1972.

Mother, by Milan Vojsk

A Slovenian mother has been taught from generation to generation, from the old country, that the most precious commodity one can buy is land. Once land is purchased, the next investment is to put a home on it.

She usually feels that charge accounts are unnecessary. She pays cash for everything—groceries, clothes, and even the family car. She will reason, "If you can't pay for it now, you don't need it!" Real estate agents have marveled about Slovenians going to the bank and paying cash for a house!

Our heroine has the best looking house in the block. There is never any dust found even in the most remote corner. She washes clothes every day. She can't stand anything dirty.

Outside the home, Slovenian mothers have been known to mow the lawn (honest), do the gardening, and trimming. But best of all, she loves her flower garden. Every home-owning family has one. She spends hours caring for flowers. And buying a rose is unthinkable. She usually borrows a cutting from a friend, plants it in the ground, and when that blooms, takes more cuttings until the yard is filled with beautiful roses.

Her life is very religious; she never misses going to church. She teaches her children the traits of honesty, and the value of maintaining a sterling character. "A man is only as good as his word," she says.

But why go on? You must know the person we are describing; she can be found almost everywhere. And she is a legend in her own time!

A mother is a mother still,
The holiest thing alive.
—Coleridge

Janko Rogelj (1895–1974)

Janko Rogelj

THE CHARTER MEMBER

Translated by Joseph Valencic

Jack Zmeda was distressed. The president's report in the lodge newspaper had stated that Jack Zmeda was a charter member of the organization. Yet the secretary's report did not even mention Jack's name. He now felt he was in a doubtful position.

The uncertainty of it all gave him quite a headache. The more he thought about the situation, the more confused he was: "The president should know 'cause he's the highest official. But the secretary should know, too, 'cause he takes care of all the records. So why don't they agree?"

What disturbed Jack the most was that he himself could not remember whether or not he was an original member of the Studenček lodge, now celebrating its fiftieth anniversary.

As Jack troubled his aching head about it, a comforting rationale began to form: "The president's word is most important because he is the head of the lodge. He is the one who holds the gavel at meetings and gives the floor to speakers. He is also the first to give his signature to lodge documents. If a member dies, it is the president who gives the eulogy. In short, he has the first and last word and would know for sure if Jack was a charter member fifty years ago."

So Jack then figured that the secretary's accounts don't mean a thing. "What could that secretary know? He isn't the chief of the lodge—he's just a humble servant!"

A large resplendent banquet was planned in honor of the charter members. The affair had great meaning for everyone, especially the founders. After spending fifty years in the lodge, they now sat at a large table, ate well and drank, and listened to educated speakers. The others looked upon their oldest brothers with respect and trust. There they were at the main table--those rare members who formed the groundwork of the lodge and had persevered to make it great.

SOURCE: Janko Rogelj, *Skrivnostni klic* (Ljubljana: Državna Založba Slovenije, 1967), 84-87.

Jack sat himself at the last table in the back of the hall. He had his approach already planned: "Act humble and inconspicuous so that when they announce your name, you can stand up and really shine. The whole place will be staring at you!"

As the banquet was starting, the president asked the founders to sit at the speakers' table. He then read off their names alphabetically. Jack Zmeda knew that his name would be the last on the list. But the president sat down after he called the name of Tony Slama. . . .

Young women in starched white uniforms carried in tureens of thin soup and platters of roasted chicken in greasy puddles. Bowls of wilting lettuce in strong vinegar were also placed on the tables. Only the vivid red beets and green peas showed any life—mainly because they were undercooked. But on the creaking tables the Slovenian "potica" reigned supreme and quickly found its way to everyone's plate. The hot coffee which finally arrived burned the guests' tongues, insuring silence as they listened to the speaker who had been brought in from some distant lodge to help honor the men.

Jack Zmeda had tears in his eyes. He had some soup, hoping that it would keep him from visibly crying. After that he could not eat anything more. His neighbors at the table tried to persuade him at least to taste some of the other food. But Jack resisted, knowing that his throat would immediately constrict from sorrow.

The question continually pounded on his brain: "Am I a charter member?" Unconsciously he pulled the formal invitation from his pocket. His name was printed among the founding members. His neighbors noticed him as he was turning the invitation in his hands. Louie Ježičnik was sitting opposite and stretched across the table to Jack.

"The invitation says you're a charter member. So what're you doin' sittin' here with us?"

Offended, Jack answered with a Scriptural saying:

"'Many are called but few are chosen.' They didn't call me even though I'm marked down as an original member. See! That's what happens when you're too long in the lodge and ready for your grave. Boy, I remember the kinda funerals they used to throw for a guy if he died at the right time. And now? Hell, if you die now, nobody goes to your funeral. And that's what's gonna happen to me 'cause I been too damn long in this lodge."

The roster of speakers was unusually long but this was necessary to satisfy all the politicians who wanted exposure at the ceremony. . . . As the speeches dragged on, Jack suddenly rose and took leave. He was glad he was not seated as a charter member because, in that case, he would have had to sit through to the end.

About six months later something unexpected happened. Jack received a newspaper clipping from Slovenia that said, among other things, that Jack was one of the founding members of the Studenček lodge. The lodge name was misspelled, but he wasn't confused by that, since it wasn't the first time a Slovenian newspaper had misprinted the title of an American organization. The point was that the article mentioned Studenček—hardly a common name for a lodge—and that Jack was a charter member of his lodge. That was enough proof for him.

He appeared at the next lodge meeting and asked for the floor. After reading the article, he assailed his fellow members:

"You hypocrites! What kind of lodge brothers are you? Even in Europe they knew that I was a charter member. And you guys didn't know!" Then he turned abruptly and left.

No reports were published on how Jack's lodge brothers were affected by his attack. But the whole matter of Jack's mix-up does show that even in Europe they read Slovenian American newspapers and pay due respect to charter members of Slovenian American fraternal lodges.

Katka Zupančič (1889–1967), by Lillian Brulc

Katka Zupančič

HOW MUCH WILL YOU GIVE?

Translated by Edward Krasovich

On the outskirts of a mid-American city stands a nondescript six-room house, built on the pattern of thousands of other American homes. Its front faces the street, and it is constructed of light-colored brick. A beautiful young maple tree stands in the center of a well-kept lawn which gives the appearance of a carpet of green. The shades are pulled halfway on the windows on whose clean panes the sun glistens.

All this is taken in with one quick glance by the man who is already up the steps and in front of the door. He rings. As he rings a second time, he hears steps on the walk along the side of the house. From around the corner appears a somewhat heavy, almost bald, well-tanned gentleman. His round, good-looking face is clean shaven.

"What do you want?" he asks sullenly, peevishly turning his gaze upward. When his caller laughs good-naturedly, the gentleman recognizes him and at once becomes friendly. "Ah, look at you! Do you know, I almost snubbed you. . . ."

"Because I interrupted your sweet dreams, no doubt! You were sleeping, weren't you?"

"Well, I was reading and dozed off. The family has gone to the movies, and I'm home alone. Come, let's go back to the patio."

As soon as they arrive there, he quickly picks up the scattered newspapers, stacks them on the table, and as he places a stone on them, he says, "That should keep Brother Wind from doing any further mischief." Just then he notices sheets of paper protruding from his friend's pocket, and half of his friendliness goes with the wind. "So be it. I'll go get you a beer anyway, even though the only time you call on me is when you're begging. . . ."

His friend was hurt. "If I do beg, I'm not begging for myself. . . ."

SOURCE: Katka Zupančič, *Slike iz vsakdanjega življenja* (Chicago: Prosvetna Matica, 1946), 102-11.

"Yes, I know," he quickly reassures him. "I could have pretended not to be at home, but I didn't," he said brusquely, and marched off into the house after the beer. For he, Joe Koppel, one-time Jozek Capelj, was proud of his reputation. He did not want to be considered stingy; that's why he always gave a little something "whenever the devil brought them over with their collection campaigns."

In the house he put a few coins into his pocket, filled two mugs with beer, and returned to the patio.

"O.K., let's drink to your health and mine, and tell me what you think of the war." He wipes the foam from his lips. "So, how do we stand? Will we or won't we? And when will there be an end to it?"

His friend laughs off the questions, saying that he is not a prophet, and that both of them hold the same beliefs. "However, if you read the reports from the old country and considered the conditions over there, you wouldn't be able to sleep nights, unless you had a heart of stone."

"Eh, war is war. It brings good to no one. One hears this, and one hears that. But no one knows the truth."

"I don't have time to get into a lengthy conversation. But I would like to emphasize something, and that is this: our people over there are being threatened with total annihilation. Do you know what that means: total annihilation? And so it behooves us to help our unfortunate countrymen over there, as many of them as survive. That is why I have come to you. . . ."

He pulled a sheet from his pocket. "How much will you give? You know, they will need a bit of everything. Mainly food, clothing, shoes, medicines, doctors. How much will you give?

"They will need tools, they will need livestock for the fields, cows for milking. How much will you give?

"They will have to begin everything from scratch. Their forests have been destroyed and burned, or their lumber has been hauled away. But they will need roofs for themselves and their livestock. How much will you give?

"For their devastated fields and gardens they will need seeds, all kinds. We'll have to give some thought to hospitals for them, and refuges, especially for their poor, orphaned children. So, tell me, how much will you give?"

It was difficult for Koppel to feign a cool indifference, and still more difficult to force a compassionate laugh. Some bitter retorts came to his tongue, but he withheld them.

His friend continued, "Their schools are destroyed, their teachers who were not caught are killed or scattered. Thousands and thousands of our countrymen are languishing in concentration camps. And if some of them should be saved, shall we let them die along the way like dumb animals? So, how much will you give?"

He became quiet and waited.

"Ha, you really know how! You don't say, 'Will you give something?' but rather, 'how much, and how much, and how much will you give?' just like a broken phonograph record. But I'll tell you straight out—you can be offended or not—I'm not giving anything. You may look surprised if you wish. If you were collecting for something over here, I'd reach into my pocket and count out something for you. But for those over there—not one red cent! It's just the principle of the thing."

"The principle? . . . The principles of sober and honest thinking people are always aimed at good. But yours are turned and twisted, like a goat's horns. Come on, talk and be guided like a man who has sense and whose heart is in the right place."

Koppel jumped as though he had been stung by a hornet. "I'd be a fool and a lunatic if I talked and were guided any differently!" His lips curled contemptuously. "You know, I always laugh when I read those tearful appeals of yours: 'Give, give, the old country calls, calls. . . .'" He made a face.

"Ah, my friend, you would not laugh at those tearful appeals if you. . . ."

"If I had stayed over there, you mean to say, don't you? But I am here, you see, here! America is an altogether different home for me than my wretched one over there was!"

"And therefore you feel no obligation to the old country, because your life there was a wretched one?"

"I'd like to know what kind of obligation! I think I served her well enough, since after I got here I brought over my two sisters, although I should have left one of them there because she is nothing but trouble for me. But that's another matter, and doesn't concern you. I wanted to get my brother over here, too. But the fool got stuck on a farm and stayed there. He wrote that he got married and is satisfied, and that everything was going well. Good, good. Perhaps he did make his bed well, but if the Germans and Italians unmade it for him —that's not my fault. I advised him to sell everything he had there and come here. But he wouldn't do it.

"So, you see, I can wash my hands even when it comes to my own blood brother."

All puffed up with pride and self-love, he stretched himself comfortably on the bench, and calmly met his friend's eyes which were piercing him sharply and almost hostilely. In his self-considered triumph, he wanted to be good-natured. "So, are you still going to try to pressure me?"

"Please don't force me to tell you what I think of you. . . ."

"Oh, so you think I'm hard-hearted, but I'm not. My youngest child can wrap me around his finger three times."

His friend kept quiet and stubbornly waited.

Koppel finally made a face, and said, "In truth, you don't understand me. You can't understand why I have no feeling

The kiss of Judas, or "I can wash my hands even when it comes to my own blood brother," by France Gorše

for our so-called brothers, nor for those celebrated 'hills and dales.' But you haven't seen them through my eyes. . . ." He sighed deeply, and reproachfully turned towards his friend, as if to say, "you judge me blindly."

"Now he is winding himself in gray sentimentality and will begin feeling sorry for himself, and will be looking for sympathy from me," thought his friend, "but I will snatch away that gray veil and tear it to shreds." Involuntarily he, too, sighed, and said:

"It seems to me that you would have seen those 'hills and dales,' with the people, in a better light if you had had some buttered white bread, isn't that so?"

Koppel threw out his arms ecstatically and cried: "Buttered white bread! . . . Merciful God! I would have been grateful for oatmeal bread. I was ten years old before I first ate white bread to satiety. And that was given to me by a strange hand. But I must tell you that it was earned, so you won't think that I was just a beggar. . . ."

His friend nodded understandingly. "So your former poverty has embittered your every thought about your homeland? . . ."

"Black, ugly, dirty poverty, and a belt which danced over my starved back like a fiery snake, and I didn't know whether I should hold the tattered pants I wore in front or back, since my nakedness showed both in front and in back." He laughed exhaustingly. "Oh, you'll never be able to comprehend how deep the wound of my youth was." After a short silence, he continued even more gloomily:

"And do you know how it all ended? Just as it was intended. By fire. Our home was destroyed by fire—it didn't belong to us anyway—our mother went with it, and with her my youngest brother. Our father succumbed that night from his burns. It was a snowy, cold, peaceful Christmas night. . . ." His lips began to tremble.

"Good Lord. Destiny certainly was not kind to you," quietly remarked his friend, deeply touched.

"No, indeed not. . . . Then after that my employment began. First came the big job of herding cows, and afterwards the bigger job as a hired hand. . . . That's the career that my sweet and good homeland had for me! And you have the nerve to expect me to help her with dollars that I have earned here. Never! It would be a sin!"

"They say that suffering ennobles a person. I, myself, have noted that people who have walked the thorny path often have a deeper understanding and feeling for the suffering of their fellow man. That's why I can't understand your narrow-mindedness. Neither can I understand why you should hold your misfortunes against the entire country. My youth wasn't worthy of envy either, but it wouldn't enter my mind to judge someone else by my father's shortcomings.

Offering, by Milan Vojsk

"My father didn't have the talents required for administration, nor indeed any luck. In addition, he became ill; when he finally recovered, the cream of his strength was gone forever, and then he became stubborn and irritable.

"Finally, my mother's patience was exhausted, and real dog days began for the family. Tensions and rumblings brought new thunderstorms. That was the atmosphere we grew up in. In other homes, holidays were a time of happiness, but at our house we dreaded them. On such days at our place, only hell had its orgies.

"Besides that, we worked hard. We strained ourselves to such an extent that we became like robots. In spite of everything we did, our home went downwards. . . ."

Koppel laughed harshly, "At our home we didn't go downwards. We couldn't. We were at the bottom. At our place I learned that a whimpering home love could not bring us to life."

His friend realized that the seed of his words had fallen on barren ground. "Do you want to hear about the fellow over there who was innocently indicted and imprisoned?"

Shuffling his papers, he continued: "When the true criminal confessed, the innocently accused had long since been in America. He had escaped prison, and fled to America under an assumed name. He is now an old man. But listen to how he accepted his bitter cup. 'Will I help? As much as I possibly can! It's just a pity that I'm not rich. Those who did me wrong are already in their graves. It's too bad that I never wrote them telling them that my love for my homeland was never great enough. They were never able to dim it even a bit.'"

That unwritten letter galled Koppel. He laughed hesitatingly, saying: "What would folks do without an ass? Wasn't even I innocently indicted? Indicted as an everlasting hired hand!

"I had this same head, and these hands! Look," his gesture took in the house and the garden, "this is what I accomplished with them here. But what could I have done over there? That's why no one can obscure the old country for me, because it never shined for me! With my first dollars earned in America I wanted to return there so that I could spit on her and all of Europe!"

"Why only on her and Europe? Why wouldn't you want to spit on the entire world? For poverty and misery are scattered throughout the whole world, and it's poverty that you want to spit upon, isn't it? And what if you had been born in poverty over here, where would you want to spit then?"

"Ah, but here everything is different. Here even beggars wear neckties. I heard that many of them even have cars and homes, some even in the better districts of town."

"Come now, pull the wool from your eyes. Can't you tell the difference between racketeering and poverty? Rather than sleep, you should drive around in your car, or walk along the streets, and at least from the outside you could see some of the miseries of the people. . . ."

"But those people are to blame for that themselves, . . ." put in Koppel.

"Of course. They are to blame because they were born in poverty! According to that logic, you yourself were to blame for your sad youth, since you didn't make provisions to be born into a well-to-do family. Fortunately, your wretched homeland taught you your letters, so why don't you read, so you'd know at least something of the seamy side of young, rich America—the richest country in the world?

"But you don't wish to stir up any smoky notions about her golden records. And why should you? Didn't she take you willingly under her wings—and you brought along your head and your strong arms, which you perhaps just picked up somewhere along the way. . . ."

"It is truly a miracle that I was able to pull myself up from such depths. You're needling me in vain. You'll never reach me. I'm dedicated to my new and only homeland with heart and soul, and her seamy side doesn't bother me at all."

"Of course not, you poor blind mouse, since you fell foolishly in love with the almighty dollar, and completely renounced your homeland which gave you life, strength, and character. And because she wasn't able to fill your table with beef, you can't forgive her even now, while the executioners nail her to the cross—how come you laugh and stare so?" His voice was shaking with anger.

"Beef, eh? You, too, have a loyalty to this country—yet your heart still beats for the old country."

"Millions of us came here for bread, or for better bread. We brought over, besides our strong bodies, hearts open to everything good, hearts which were not empty, nor corruptible. I don't believe in the kind of devotion which is based on money, and measured by the value of a house and garden and beef. For that is no longer realism, but merely stiff, hard-hearted egoistical materialism.

"So you're the one who cries: To whom and why? It's not our fault . . . we have no obligations toward them. . . . Who has helped, or would help us, if. . . .

"It was not idealism, nor realism, but rather materialism, which drove Judas Iscariot to sell Christ for thirty pieces of silver. . . ."

He picked up his hat, firmly determined that he would not say another word.

But Koppel felt offended. Almost angrily he reproached his friend for his offenses, the turn-arounds, and belittlings. "I a materialist? And my thoughts only on money? And all because I won't have anything to do with my homeland, which had nothing for me but a kick in the pants. For, you see, too long I prayed in vain for my daily bread. . . ."

"Which you finally got, otherwise you wouldn't be here today. And if you are honest—I say: if you are honest—you should return that little which you received. You ought to make at least one little child there happy, one who is suffering more pain and woes than you or any one of us ever did. And so I ask you for the last time: how much will you give?"

Koppel just gaped, took in a deep breath, and exhaled forcibly through his nostrils, as though he wanted to say: "Now look, we're right back where we started from!"

He mumbled something and closed his eyes, "Oh, the devil! Give me your address. Perhaps I'll mail you a small check. . . . But don't ever think that I've been taken in by your sentimentality, which attempts to save an old pot which has always leaked, and always will."

"The pot leaks all right. What was in it is the treasure we want to save. We would like to save our generation for our country, and our country for our generation. And that, my friend, is not sentimentality."

John Modic

John Modic

BEING NAKED IS A SIN

"Oh, my, somebody is walking around naked," skinny aunt Rose said loudly in Slovenian.

"Who does?" her brother, a fat little man with great drooping mustaches that almost covered his puffy cheeks, hollered from the kitchen where he sat reading the *Amerikanski Slovenec* and enjoying a Saturday afternoon of rest.

"Who dares to walk around in my house naked?" As he shouted, his huge whiteshirted belly trembled slightly where it rolled over his wide belt. He held the paper away from him expectantly, "Who?"

"Nobody," his sister shouted back triumphantly, "nobody except your own son, Joseph. He is crouching here before me; now he jumps in the air like a demon!" There was a loud "thump" as Joey hit the floor and a succession of louder noises as aunt Rose shouted like a sports announcer, "Now he is running up and down the room! Now he is hurling himself against the door! You had better come and see what has happened to your son!"

"Is he possessed?" her brother asked, still declining to get up from his chair. "For, if he is, I can do no good. Only a priest can deal with a possessed person." He chuckled at his little joke and turned back to his paper, satisfied with his decision, hoping that his sister would let well enough alone.

But aunt Rose, bony aunt Rose, was far from satisfied. She started in again. "No doubt, the neighbors are interested in your son's strange actions even if you are not. I can see Mrs. Petkovic looking in from her house. After all, it's not everyday she can see a naked boy dancing by our windows—I can't blame her."

"Why don't you pull down the shades then, if she's looking in; why don't you, eh?" he asked angrily.

"In broad daylight, pull down the shades? Mrs. Petkovic would call the police at such goings on."

"Damn Mrs. Petkovic! Do I run my household for her benefit, the old busybody? Let her turn her eyes in shame before

SOURCE: *Skyline*, vol. 20, no. 1, 1948, 3-4.

God punishes her—staring at naked boys," he finished on a note of great indignation.

The sounds of running and jumping from the living room where Joey was nicely ignoring his aunt became livelier.

"He is running fiercely now," his aunt called out. "Soon he will fall out of a window."

"Joseph," his father yelled in some exasperation, "please, why don't you stop for awhile, sit on our fine sofa, rest yourself, tomorrow is another day."

"Put on a pair of pants, Joseph," aunt Rose added.

The busy sounds continued.

"See, I could be a stone on the ground for all he listens to me," she said in a hurt voice calculated to affect her brother.

"Joseph," her brother shouted as he turned a page with a moistened thumb, "listen to your aunt more carefully in the near future."

Joey spoke up for the first time. "Aunt Rose is full of hops," he said definitely. "She don't understand what I'm doing, that's all." He spoke in English; this increased his aunt's bitterness since she understood only a small portion of what he said.

"And now," she mourned, "your son curses me; that is my reward after all this time."

"He doesn't curse you," his father corrected; "he just said that you were filled with, with—"

"Hops," Joey supplied.

"Yes, hoops," his father said easily. He was very proud of his mastery of the English tongue.

"Up to the neck," said Joey.

"I have spent five years taking care of your house and children since your wife died, and this is the thanks I get, a naked boy calling me names."

"All right, all right." Her brother raised himself reluctantly; the fat over his belt rolled up and made his paunch a thing of beauty again, firm and round under his shirt.

He walked grumbling into the living room. His sister was sitting primly in an armchair, an expression of distaste on her thin, long-nosed face, as she watched her nephew in a bright yellow basketball suit, pivot and then break for an imaginary basket on the wall over the door leading to a bedroom.

"Look at him—naked!" she said pointing dramatically as Joey shot from mid-floor and then followed up for the backboard play. The back of his jersey showed dark wet spots around the big number "3" that was sewed on between the lettering MISTEK & SONS and FUNERAL DIRECTORS.

"Rose," Joey's father said reproachfully, "anyone can see he is not all naked; he has underwear on, has he not?"

"Naked," she said firmly, "a twelve-year-old naked boy, and acting like a lunatic."

"But he is just running and jumping, having a good time."

"I'm practicing," Joey remarked as he made another long shot.

"Yes, he is building himself up, exercise, exercise," his father explained patiently, but aunt Rose shook her head and made little clicking noises of disgust with her mouth.

"No good will ever come of such things," she said ominously.

Joey's father seemed to notice something for the first time. "Joseph, my boy, why are you wearing yellow underwear? In fact," he continued puzzled, "where did you get yellow underwear with numbers and letters all over it?"

Joey threw a hard overhand pass to a teammate by the victrola, dashed over to the far end of the sofa, received the return pass, and flipped a pretty pivot shot out of the three second circle before he got time to answer in a winded voice. "It ain't underwear, pa; it's a basketball suit. I'm on the Unknowns, a team at the bathhouse."

He tapped his index finger against his chest where a giant, wrinkled question mark adorned the cotton jersey. Then he cleverly feinted his father out of position, dribbled by him, and sank a basket on the other side of the room.

"You gotta be on your toes all the time in this game, pa," he said professionally as his father wheeled about in surprise.

Without stopping his activity, Joey very rapidly explained more of the game to his father.

Then his father turned to aunt Rose and said, "You see, it's nothing. It's a game where the boys jump into baskets. It is nothing—nothing to worry about—just an American game. And Joseph," he added proudly, "is number three in the bathhouse."

Aunt Rose snorted unpleasantly, got up, and went into the kitchen to start supper.

Her brother shrugged his shoulders as if to say, "what can you do with a woman like that." He went back to the *Amerikanski Slovenec*, his belly rolled down concealing his belt; he sighed profoundly and moistened his thumb preparatory to turning a page. Behind him aunt Rose banged the kitchen utensils without mercy.

"All the same, being naked is a sin," she snapped.

He did not answer.

In the living room, Number Three chalked up two more points for the Unknowns.

Stanley P. Zupan

Stanley P. Zupan

THE CROSS-SPIDER

Night lay in the offing as dusk settled over the Alleghenies. At the base of the mountain, Francel, a boy of twelve years, walked to a woodshed. He stamped through the leaves as he pierced the sagging mist. But he knew the path well. So often had he traversed it that his hobnailed boots would slink into the earth almost of their own accord. He shuffled on, swinging his arms in a rhythm of discontent. A buzzing hum, dominated by the twang of crickets, filled the valley. Francel turned to look at the house, rubbing one sleeve under his nose. From the chimney issued no smoke, only a few sparks which flashed against the dark background. The words of his foster mother echoed in his mind: "Be off, Francel! Your food! You expect to live on air? Off to the woodshed and fill the bin!"

"Live on air?" he thought as he inhaled the harvest fragrance. Trees were everywhere, while shadows massed themselves and rose bluntly upward. Here he was enveloped in mountains, while night's prelude hushed the valley in preparation for the parade of shadows, moonlight, and stars. In a short while, the bark of the neighbors' dog would no longer be muffled in the damp fogginess.

The youth carried an armful of kindling, leaning forward as he ambled toward the kitchen doorway where a voice strained forth in sharp cadences: "Francel, you imp! Plague on you, hurry!"

A woman, bobbing a pointed nose up and down and fastening her headshawl about her, met him at the door. "You sluggard!" she screeched, pulling his ear. "Quick! In the bin with that wood!"

Francel dropped the sticks into the box and crouched for a moment as would a beaten puppy. Then he turned and slapped his foster mother to loosen her hold as she pinched his ear. In a flash, he dropped to the floor in supplication, expecting a horsewhipping.

SOURCE: *Skyline*, vol. 9, no. 1, 1936, 12-14.

National Art Gallery—Adelaide, Australia

"Bonjour tristesse," by Milan Vojsk

The pocked cheeks of the woman became flushed. Every wrinkle grew taut like the chiseled lines in a granite statue, and she stared as with the eyes of a corpse. Then she gritted her teeth, while panting, "Beat you? Kick you? Murder you?" She bent over. "Nay! Too good, that!" With an upward motion of her loosely sleeved arm, and as with the gesture of a maestro signifying a crescendo with his baton, she motioned to him and yelled, "Up to bed! Nothing to eat for you! Beat you? Nay! You know the punishment for striking a mother. Before the new moon shines over the valley, your arm will wither away!"

The lad looked up. He bit his nails and shook his head, his light hair brushing his forehead as he nodded in the negative.

"No, no, no!" he gasped. "Why did I do it? Take it back, Mother! Take it back! Take it back!"

The woman laughed as the boy fell forward sobbing and buried his head in his arms. "Lucky for you the master's not home! You would not have to wait till the new moon."

From beyond came a moaning cry. She composed herself and shuffled out, mumbling, "Ah, Joshko, the master will bring the doctor! You will get well."

Francel, pale and terrified, heard the woman question in the other room: "Why did we take you to market? Why did you drink from that polluted pool? Oh, the master! When will he come? Why didn't this happen to that ingrate?" She pointed to the room she had just left.

Francel thought of the slap and of the moon, as he rubbed his arm. A knock on the door interrupted his thoughts. As three shawled women entered, the boy walked to a bench in the corner, stopping at the table to pick up a crumb with a moistened finger.

"And how is he, Mariana?" the visitors asked in unison, as Mariana entered the kitchen. Two of them gesticulated forcefully, while the third stood with folded arms.

"Does he still shiver and shake?" one asked.

"I fear," Mariana whined, "if the master does not return soon, Joshko will—"

"But it is a six-hour walk over the mountain to town," one of the women interrupted her, "and he just went before sunset!"

"Yes," another added, "and what did he do? Do you hear him wailing?" She turned her head toward the room where the sick boy lay.

Mariana brought her hands upward, saying, "Something must be done, something, something!"

With an air of assurance, one of the women questioned, "The cross-spider! Have you tried it?"

"Cross-spider!" Mariana exclaimed. "But it's too late now! They're already in hiding. Only by a stroke of good fortune could we find one at this time of year."

Francel cringed as he remembered his foster mother's curse. He looked about the corners of the ceiling for a cobweb. It was futile, however, in the immaculate house.

"Come, let us see him!" said one of the women as she started toward the sickroom.

Francel tiptoed out of the kitchen, the echo of murmuring chatter resounding in his ears as he closed the door. "Back to the woodshed!" he thought.

Outside, the air was crisp and cool. The moon lighted up the whole valley. He did not grope for the pathway but followed a winding rut of grayness, crossed by shadows. Above, the stars dotted the heavens. As much as he had detested the trip to the shed a short while before, just so much he now seemed to enjoy the walk. There was hope in his pace. The cross-spider! He would find one in the shed. Yes, not one but two! One for Joshko and one for himself. He had heard the cross-spider could remove a curse. From the kitchen window, a beam of light, interrupted by the shadows of the women pacing across, fell diagonally over the ground. Little did he suspect the women had captured a spider such as he himself hoped to find.

Francel climbed over stacks of wood to the topmost corners in the shed. Occasionally he wiped his face to brush away a dangling cobweb. For the first time in his life, he was intent on aiding his stepbrother. He had to find a cross-spider! The rest would be easy. He would dry it hurriedly over the fire, powder it, and then dissolve it in water. There was no taste to it, so they said. He would find one! But it was dark, and he dared not strike a light. From corner to corner he groped for cobwebs until he felt a crawling sensation on his face. He brought a hand to his cheek and scurried down the woodpile out-of-doors. Moonlight revealed a luminous cross on the back of a squirming spider as Francel unfolded his fingers cautiously, lest his prey escape. He ran to the house, stumbling and coughing, for the dust in the shed had choked him.

With his hand clasped firmly, he stole into the kitchen. From the sickroom came a low hum of voices. Francel stopped at the table, reached for the glass of water he found there, and gulped down the liquid. No sooner had he put the goblet back than the four women stood before him.

Three of the figures stared at the glass. Now in echo fashion, then in a chorus, they shrieked, "The goblet! He drank it! The spider!"

At first Mariana stood motionless. Then her whole body trembled.

Francel was terrified as is a rabbit surrounded by dogs. He clutched at his throat with one hand and extended his fist, without speaking. Perspiration beaded his forehead. With quick motions of the head, he looked about the room. Then he focused his eyes on the kitchen door, turned about, began to run, and tripped.

The four women buried their faces in their hands to shield from view a blotch of crimson on the edge of the hearth. The boy lay motionless on the floor. From his half-opened palm, a cross-spider squeezed out and ambled away, unnoticed. Only a moaning sound from beyond broke the silence.

Ted Kramolc, self-portrait

Ted Kramolc

AMBUSH

The skies hung dark and low. The weather forecast called for snow. Fred fiddled with the stainless steel knobs on the stereo set, to find his favorite station, to hear the weather confirmed by Stan what's-his-name. He could never remember the name, only the announcer's voice, deep, clear, not nasal, neither British nor snobbish, not quite Ontario, but "with it," broad yet not prairie. The voice was straight from the diaphragm, not an official CBC voice, yet Canadian, distinctive, recognizable. It was a manly voice; he always waited for it. Once or twice he saw Stan on TV doing a hockey game commentary, but the face didn't fit the voice. So he preferred to listen to him on the stereo. The voice said that there was to be rain tomorrow.

Fred could have saved himself the trouble, for he knew that the rain was due. His back hurt—an injury from the last war. He always hurt before rain.

His sons came over to his bed. When the back hurt, Fred always went to bed. This time it hurt bad. He would hide the warming pad under the blanket. Sympathy irritated him.

"Are we going skiing tomorrow, Daddy?" They both looked excited.

"Have you waxed the skis?" he asked.

"Yes," they both answered.

"The boots, the poles, and the ski gloves? Is everything ready for tomorrow?"

"Yes, yes!"

"I don't want any delay in the morning. Be up at eight o'clock so that we can hit the slopes when the tows open!"

"Will you tuck us in, Daddy?" They never asked their mother to do this, and it gave him pleasure. There was really no tucking in to do, since Bill always slept in the sleeping bag for some strange reason and Paul was always covered up to the chin anyway by the time he got around to tucking him in. It was merely a ritual.

Prepared especially for this anthology.

Archaic landscape, by Ted Kramolc

"Good night, Billy! Good night, Paul!" They were his boys, long past the tucking-in age, yet he bent down over their beds and kissed them each on their cheek, slapped their bottoms and turned off the light in both bedrooms.

As if to postpone their falling asleep—"What's the skiing going to be like, Daddy? Is it going to be O.K.?"

"It's going to be perfect?"

"You sure?"

"Yah!"

"Good night, Daddy!"

"Good night, Billy! Good night, Paul!"

At that moment the family cat came in and they both wanted to sleep with it.

* * *

It rained the next day. The announcer on the radio said that there was no skiing that weekend anywhere in Southern Ontario. Fred took the boys to see a matinee picture show, returned home, and said to his wife,

"I think I'll be going downtown to tour the art galleries."

"Fine," she replied, for she did not care for contemporary painting.

* * *

Fred parked the car behind Bloor Street, walked over to the area where the art galleries abound and viewed a couple of boring exhibitions. Bent pieces of multicolored plastic pipe fastened on polished wood . . . pictorial emptiness. It was late afternoon and he felt hungry, so he ate a sandwich, washed down with a beer at one of the coffee houses. He then lit a cigar. It did not taste right. He left it smoldering in the cheap ashtray, and with his hands buried deep in his ski jacket stepped out into the gray wet street.

Yorkville Street was busy despite the steady drizzle. Young people hung around corners, leaned against wet tree trunks, shuffled restlessly in small circles—three or four in a group as if expecting a confidential messenger to arrive with decisive news. Some walked up and down the same side of the street, retracing their footsteps, not unlike a great driver cutting corners on a Formula I race circuit. Longhairs, beardniks, young unkempt girls, their manes resembling stiff strands of dusty hay, swinging their hips in wrinkled frayed levis.

It was too cold for the sidewalk coffee cafes to be open, yet some bearded hippies sat on a few metal chairs that had been left there from the Fall. A policeman, walking almost in the middle of the street as if he were afraid he would become contaminated, smiled in labored benevolence; receiving little attention, he soon turned the corner and was out of sight. The majority of people in this crowd were youths who resembled beats, but were not. Many of the girls wore flowery pants, Apache headbands, loud colored scarves and weird looking coats, but their clothes looked tailored and even when disarrayed, one could see the studied, arranged sloppiness. Their eyes clear, quite unlike the true acid heads; long hair shiny, skin healthy. They belonged — some did, the others only thought they did — to this "in crowd." Such was the vogue of the day.

They frequented the "Village" primarily because of the small smart shops where one could find clothes and items that differed from the standard merchandise offered for sale in the established department stores. They were the ones who added color and excitement to Yorkville. These young people kept coffee houses, shops, and tiny restaurants going. The real beats were — despite their way-out mumblings, flowery garments, beards, and beads — gray people, forever broke.

Fred came down here because of the two galleries that exhibited his graphic work. He enjoyed watching the people, but he hated the coffee shops. These houses, as they were called, charged atrocious prices for ordinary tasting coffee. Some had half-naked waitresses serving to patrons who reaked of phony interests in art, the supernatural, the occult. Walls were decorated with nostalgic artifacts, music — the latest "Shankar."

He smiled at a couple of blond girls passing by. The one closer to him, with white vinyl boots halfway up her thighs, black miniskirt not longer than fourteen inches, open leather jacket over the loosely buttoned jersey, smiled back and then with a toss of her full head of hair leaned over to her girl-friend, said something, both looking back, laughing, waving at him.

For a split second he wanted to go over to them. Just then he caught a glimpse of himself in a store window. Lean, tall, and long hair graying at the temples hanging over the upturned collar of his dark green ski jacket.

I must have my hair cut, he thought, brushing the full sideburns back over his ears. He fussed with the bulky white Irish fisherman's sweater his wife had given him for Christmas. He pulled it down, smoothing it over his narrow black trousers. He felt fit. He looked around but the two blond girls had disappeared.

Wanting to see a show by a Quebec artist, he suddenly found himself in a walk-down shop filled with crazy neckties, scarves, and artifacts. The sweet sickly smell of burning Chinese incense sticks made him leave quickly. He wandered next into a poster shop full of kids, viewing the posters, a few buying, counting out their money with great care. The clerk behind a makeshift counter, long hair untrimmed with a beard to match and smiling with a mouth full of decayed teeth, suggested he buy a nice poster of Castro, Mao, or Che. They were nice, the clerk said, and because of constant handling and being a bit frayed at the edges—"Half price!"

"I don't dig worn merchandise," answered Fred. The clerk's smile vanished. A few people even turned around. He left quickly.

* * *

Fred returned to the parking lot, paid the attendant, and started up, determined to get loaded in a nearby bar. What else was there to do on a day such as this had been? Perhaps I'll go and see a movie again, he thought. But he had never enjoyed seeing a film by himself and the realization that he wouldn't be able to enjoy himself, being alone, made him irritable. He slammed the gearshift into first and released the clutch so fast that the car leaped forward, almost knocking down a traffic sign. Halfway out of the parking lot, he heard somebody call his name. He slipped the clutch, slowed, and rolled down the window halfway. He heard his name being called out again. Pulling over to the curb, he noticed in the side mirror a girl running over to his car.

"Fred! Hey, Fred! Hello, Fred!" The girl was now at the side of the car. The curb was high with slushy snow which had come suddenly during the rain in the earlier hours of the afternoon. All he could see were her legs. He looked down and then up her dark stockinged thighs, the short leather miniskirt. The legs below the knees in tightly laced motorcycle boots looked delicious. He leaned out of the window, but still could not see her face. She was standing too close. He got out of the car excitedly. Who in hell would recognize him in this crowd!

The girl was of standard height. Her hair was not a mane in the fashion of the day, but neatly cut and short. A wide flowery headband tied behind the ear cascaded freely down her shoulders. She was slim and looked animated.

Fred stepped closer, his eyes scanning the young face. The tip of her nose had a slight upward slant and higher up was a tiny scar that looked almost pretty. The girl smiled, the tip of her tongue on the moist lower lip. Only one girl had a mouth like this one. The corners of it curved down gently and then up. Nelson Eddy, the singing movie star of the forties, had a smile like hers. He had told her that once, but she was too young or too disinterested in the past to remember the stars of yesterday.

"Cynthia!" he cried out.

"Hello, Fred!"

A warm feeling embraced him. The girl had always called him "Mr. Novak" before this.

He moved closer to the girl and embraced her. Her hands were on his shoulders, her hair touching his face.

"You look great, Cynthia! You look sensational!" said Fred as he held her at elbow's length. He stepped back a little, his hands firm on her hips.

"You're beautiful, gorgeous!"

The girl laughed.

"You've grown since, . . ." he almost said, but that was how one spoke to children. He felt his palms getting a tighter hold on her waist.

"Your headband is nice. No Apache ever looked so good! You crazy, sexy kid."

"I'm no kid!" replied Cynthia, the tip of her wet tongue again on her lower lip. Her eyes never left Fred's face as she spoke to him. They were blue-gray, mischievous and sparkling. The eyes of a woman. The kind of eyes that look gray and dark when melancholy clouds them and sadness washes away the spark. There was a hint of eyeshadow, a touch of silver on the lids, eyelashes heavy with mascara. He couldn't stop looking at her —the youthful face, the slender neck, high breasts, dark full thighs. There was a light sweet fragrance in her hair.

"Ambush?" he asked. "Right?"

She nodded, a flush of color suddenly rushing up her neck to her cheeks.

A summer ago, he had driven her home after she had babysat his two sons. It was early morning, the air still cool . . . first streaks of orange light low on the horizon, the suburban homes appearing like purple silhouettes and television towers on the roofs looking like exclamation points. She had let him hold her hand, squeeze it gently, and he had wondered jokingly about the perfume she had on.

"Had a lot to drink?" she asked.

"Enough. What are you wearing? It smells very nice."

"It's called Ambush."

"Ambush? Where, where?" Fred looked around in mock panic, as they drove on. "Do you always wear perfume when you babysit?"

"Not always." She squeezed his hand firmly, looking straight ahead into the orange light of the early dawn.

Lost for words, he held her hand, driving on, a strange desire flooding his loins.

"How was Christmas?" asked Fred, his face aglow . . . his eyes submerged in hers.

"Fine."

"I haven't wished you a happy new year yet—have I?"

He bent over and kissed her. His hand moved up to her breasts, his thumb sliding over the silky surface of her blouse. He felt the nipples become hard. She had then instinctively kissed him back. He stepped back, away from her.

It was only then that he noticed a young fellow standing a few feet away from Cynthia.

"This is Bill," she said awkwardly.

"Oh, how are you, Bill?"

"Very well, sir."

The boy's handshake was firm. His face pleasant, unmarked by life—the type of face one cannot remember for long.

It was the eyes that disturbed Fred. They were clear, the color of blue ice. He always had trouble reading blue eyes. There was a faint smile on the boy's lips.

Fred felt himself lost for words. He always felt proud of his ability to establish a quick rapport with young people. He felt young most of the time; that was probably why.

It was that smile on the boy's face that must have made him self-conscious.

He looked at Cynthia, her cheeks and now her neck turning red.

Sensing Fred's uneasiness, she said awkwardly:

"What are you doing down here, Fred? I mean here in the midst of all these hippies?"

"It's because of the rain. We always ski weekends." He told her about the art galleries.

"We saw a couple of shows ourselves just now, didn't we, Bill?"

Bill nodded, that smile still on his lips.

"Was there anything that you like?" asked Fred.

"Yah, I liked Riopelle," said Cynthia. "I think his work is groovy—you know, the colors, the way he slaps the paint on. I would just love to own one of his paintings! But the prices! Wow!"

She was Cynthia again, smiling, animated.

"I like Riopelle myself," Fred said. "At least the buyer gets a lot of paint for his money."

"Oh, you're terrible, Fred!" laughed the girl, brushing a lock of hair away from her mouth.

"I saw six exhibitions this afternoon, yet I don't think I could recall one damn painting right now. It's like a cocktail party. A lot of senseless, idiotic talk, a lot of elegant-looking people smiling around fragrant limbs, latest coiffures. An hour later, nobody remembers what was said and what the people there looked like. I, for one, can never recall a single face from those silly social gatherings."

Fred was getting excited now.

"I really don't know why all these people paint. It's all anti-art, anti-hero stuff, full of pseudo-Freudian symbolism. I'm convinced that most of these artists—if one can call them that—hate art and themselves. Themselves, mostly. Because, you see, painting is nothing more than a synthesis of the artist's personal philosophy of life, expressed through graphic or painting media—providing the painter has mastered his craft first.

"There's a showing on now, a few blocks north of here. You've got to see it! The joint they call a gallery is full

Courtesy of News, Ltd., Mirror Australian Telegraph Publications

Gallery, by Stanislaus Rapotec

of two-by-fours. All lumber! All over the floor. Imagine, unfinished lumber, green spruce, neatly spaced on the floor, and a plank or two to walk over. And, oh yeah, a few pieces leaning against the wall, spotlit from above to create a few shadows, all very mysterious, all very deep. In any damn lumberyard. . . . Oh, well, I got carried away. I always do, talking about painting."

"Do you still paint a lot?" asked Cynthia.

"Yes, but—not really that much. I'm looking for a new gallery to show my work. The owner of the place that represented me died. I've got to find myself a new dealer.

"The whole art scene is, well, just a scene. You work your ass off for a couple of years or longer, working evenings, weekends, whenever you can steal a free moment. You neglect your family, you suffer because of it, and then your work gets hung for a couple of weeks. The opening comes and you find yourself smiling like some Doris Day to all kinds of people, breaking your backside to be polite and pleasant so that they will buy. Oh, well, it's a racket. And at the same time you wish that these same people would overlook the one painting or two that you yourself consider good, so that when loneliness and uncertainties rush in on you, you have something to fall back on, something to fight that id in you that questions you: 'Why in hell do you bother, Mac? Is it really worth it?'

"But the best work always sells and you're left with only the money. You spend that and there's nothing to show for your long hours of work. Oh, well!"

Fred looked at Cynthia. Was there a faint look of admiration in her eyes? Or was it only compassion? Instinctively he knew that the girl liked him, but she would never say so. But then, he thought, could this be just a projection of his own wishes? Christ, the girl was at least twenty years younger!

He was losing his perspective and he knew it.

Bill broke the silence.

"You mentioned something about the anti-hero image in contemporary art. What do you mean by 'anti-hero,' sir?"

The "sir" at the end of the question irritated Fred.

"Are you thinking of becoming a painter yourself?"

"No, sir!" There was that goddamned smile again.

"Oh, what's your bag then?"

"Student."

"College? What are you in?"

"Engineering," answered Bill.

"I wish that I were." Immediately Fred wished he hadn't said that. He knew without looking up that the boy's smile broadened. Fred knew that he could read the boy's eyes now, ice-blue or not, unless the boy were a fantastic actor. Nobody is that good an actor at the age of twenty. Fred not only sensed, he knew what Bill thought of him. That smile shrouded in a whimsical politeness was not politeness at all. He

Doghouse, by Ted Kramolc

remembered looking at his father that same way once, a long time ago, when he caught him fondling their maid.

Fred knew that Bill wanted him to say something square, something reactionary—anything to discredit himself in the girl's eyes.

It bothered him that he felt compelled to answer the young man's challenge. Couldn't he just as well look at his watch, excuse himself, and be on his way?

"Well," he said finally, after a lengthy pause, as if to give the following words more meaning, "an anti-hero is the epitome of the alienated modern man, confused, guilt-ridden, driven, unable to trust his instincts, or anyone, anymore. Scared of love, never really having been warmed by love, ergo, unable to radiate love himself, he revolts, strikes out in a blind rage, ridiculing what he subconsciously craves, destroying the very food his soul is screaming for. It is his final destruction that we identify with, that we shed our tears for; it helps to wash our guilt feelings, our sins, away.

"The anti-art artist negates the process of creation and is a failure before he even begins. In painting I like painters like Bounard, Picasso, Kokoshka. Especially Kokoshka! To me, these guys represent the hero. . . ."

Fred began to feel uneasy. "The description of an anti-hero sounded a bit pompous," he thought, "but it impressed Cynthia!"

Still he went on, a racer carried along by momentum.

"In entertainment, in the movies," he said, "Errol Flynn! There was a hero!"

"He's dead!" said the boy.

"All right, Gary Cooper!"

"He's dead!" said the boy again.

"Spencer Tracy!"

"He's dead, too! All those guys are dead!"

"John Wayne!"

"John Wayne? You must be kidding, sir! That right-wing old square!"

"He's a real man! To me, at least! Tall, two-fisted, upright, simple, happy!" answered Fred, a strange hoarseness gripping his voice. "Why in hell am I talking about all these entertainment people, these specimens from a plastic menagerie created by Hollywood moneymakers?" he thought.

The girl was silent, standing exactly between the two of them, looking at one and then at the other, one of her hands on her hip, the other at her lips, as if to conceal the pleasure of witnessing, perhaps for the first time in her life, the battle of two males for a female. For her!

"Whom do you like, Cynthia?"

"Oh, I don't know," said the girl. "Well, I like the guy who had the lead in 'Love Story,' Ryan O'Neal. He's great!"

"Why him?" asked Fred.

"He's sensitive, no hang-ups, he's young," said Bill.

The emphasis was on "young." "The bastard is hitting below the belt," thought Fred.

"Yeah," Fred said aloud, "he's that all right!"

Bill's lips were pressed together into the thin, broad smile of a hunter about to strike the mortal blow.

"I wish that we could talk some more, go somewhere, have a drink together."

"That would be nice, huh, Bill?" the girl said.

"We are both under age, sir," replied Bill. "You wouldn't want any trouble, would you?"

"O.K. then, it's getting late, ah—it's been nice seeing you again, Cynthia. See you sometime! See you, Bill!"

"Sure!" said the girl. "See you!"

Bill said nothing.

* * *

It started to snow. Thick, wet snowflakes covered the ugly gray of the sidewalk, his, everybody's shoulders, hair.

Fred's eyes followed the girl as she walked away slowly, holding Bill's hand, stepping over lumps of ice and snow, avoiding the oncoming people. By the way she walked, Fred knew that she felt his stare. But she didn't turn around and soon they were both out of his sight.

* * *

Fred moved suddenly, cat-like, jumped over the high bank of snow, slid, almost fell on the slushy pavement, regained his balance, and got in the car.

He drove off up the main street to the highway and turned west, toward home.

The road was slippery, yet he drove fast.

The Islington Avenue intersection came up, then the Kipling cutoff, suddenly; he slowed down too late. He was going into the turn too fast. Halfway through the curve he realized that he wouldn't make it.

The car began to swerve sideways, the steering wheel correction not helping much. Spinning around, the car hit the embankment of snow made by the snow plough, hard; it shook him up, stunning him. Fred hit the brakes, but this only made matters worse, and he came to a stop in the ditch.

"Are you all right, sir? Are you all right?"

"Yes, I'm fine!" A face came into focus, slowly, a cop's face. Brushing the hair off his own face, Fred reached into his breast pocket for his driver's license, as requested.

"Here it is, officer!"

"Have you been drinking?"

"No, sir!"'

"O.K., O.K.," said the cop, handing him back the papers. "I'll get the tow truck for you sir! You sure need a towtruck!"

"Thanks, very kind of you! Thanks!"

"Damn weather!"

The cop, calling in on his radio, waved at Fred and drove off.

Fred rolled the window down all the way.

The snow had turned into sleet. The sharp, frozen particles biting Fred's face made him blink and shade his eyes.

A scent hung on the palm of his hand. Light, sweet, distinct. The perfume brought back Cynthia's image. Her hair brushing his cheek, the feel of her breast under his hand. The loose end of her Indian headband floating freely, kite-like in the breeze, caressing his forehead, kissing her own neck, drawing tiny, crazy designs on her shoulders.

"Goddamn weather! Damn broad!"

He ran his hands down his trousers as if to rub off the smell of the perfume. He got out of the car, his legs a bit unsteady. He bent over, picked up a mound of snow, and rubbed it on his hands. It didn't erase the scent.

Back in the car, with the window still open, he sat and listened to the staccato of the frozen rain on the metal roof. He tried to think. He leaned back.

"It's going to be a while before the tow truck comes. Yeah, in this weather it's going to be some time."

He sat there silently, waiting.

He thought, trying to sort out the events of the day.

It was getting dark.

For the first time in his life—the very first time—he didn't feel young anymore.

Composition, by H. Gregory Prusheck (Perušek)

IV

A SOUL DIVIDED

Ivan Jontez, by Nancy Bukovnik

Ivan Jontez

A SOUL DIVIDED

Translated by Joseph Kess

Alesh Prosen dreamed strange dreams. Suitcase in hand, with light steps, he hurried along the path through the green fields which led from the railroad station to the small country village, a fifteen-minute walk away. He had not seen the village for twenty years now. It was a sunny spring day and Carniola displayed herself in her smartest outfit. The fields were a succulent green, the meadows were sprinkled with gaily colored flowers, the gardens were transformed into lovely nosegays, and the whisper of birdsong tinkled throughout the forest. The mountains and Alpine meadows were covered in green and in the background the azure heavens were pierced by the gray snowy caps crowning the jagged giants of the Karavanken and Julian Alps. This was indeed a beautiful picture for the emigrant returning home.

Alesh stopped, a good rifle-shot away from the first village house. Kramar's old hayrack was heavily laden and was defying the wind with great difficulty. "Such beauty," he cried out with delight, as he drank in the sight of his native land.

"And I thought that this little piece of God's earth had no more attraction for me, that it no longer suited me. What a mistake! Of course, twenty years of living abroad erased this beautiful picture from my memory. The black smoke of American factory chimneys obscured it so that I couldn't see it anymore. Now I see how I deluded myself! My God, how beautiful this small corner of the earth is! How pleasing the sight of it is to my eyes!"

The suitcase slipped from his hand. His chest swelled, his face glowed with an inner happiness, and his eyes eagerly drank in the beauty which surrounded him.

"Magnificent!"

SOURCE: Ivan Jontez, "Razklane duše," *Ameriški Družinski Koledar*, 1935, 24-29.

Madonna with Child, by Steven A. Rebeck

Alesh felt great contentment in his heart, so much so that a terrible temptation came over him—a temptation to yodel exuberantly, as he had done time and time before in the days of his youth. He wanted to yodel right across the fields and meadows so that the echo would resound off the mountains. And he would have done so, if he had not thought that such a thing was unbecoming to a man of his years and position. Instead, he muzzled his sudden desire and ashamedly pushed it back into the recesses of his soul.

"Am I crazy?" he asked and he grew angry with himself. His emotions had made him feel ashamed. "Just like a child, like some foolish young boy!"

Then on the path ahead he noticed a male figure approaching him directly.

"Perhaps it's one of my old acquaintances," Alesh said to himself happily, picking up his suitcase and starting toward his native village and apparent friend from the past. When Alesh and the stranger were still about ten paces from one another, the stranger stopped in front of an old stone wayside shrine. It was before this same shrine to Mary, the Mother of God, that Alesh had taken leave of the village twenty years ago.

Alesh also stopped and stood in amazement. This man was a stranger and yet he looked so remarkably familiar. Was it an old friend? He didn't look like any of them. Alesh realized suddenly that the stranger leaning against the stone shrine, silently staring at him, closely resembled Alesh himself. True, he was slightly more peasant-like and his face was burned from the sun. Otherwise, they were as similar as two peas in a pod.

"Amazing," Alesh said to himself, and lingered for a moment, hesitating whether he should speak or whether he should wait to let the man take the initiative. He decided to speak first. Just as he was about to open his mouth to greet the stranger, a mysterious thing happened. He stood rooted to the spot as if he had been turned into stone.

The figure of still another stranger sprang forth from Alesh. This stranger was in all respects as identical to the first stranger as Alesh himself. It was as if the three of them had been born of the same mother at the same instant. And when the strangers came together they behaved as if all had been agreed upon beforehand. They reached their arms out one to the other. Around their mouths played smiles of delight and in their eyes burned the fire of fierce celebration.

"Welcome back to your native soil!" exclaimed the first.

"My warmest greetings, dear friend!" delightedly replied the second.

The strangers embraced one another warmly.

"How have you fared? How has it been all these years?" the first was eager to know.

"In the beginning it was difficult, but now it's not too bad," the second replied with a smile, and again drew the first to him in embrace.

Alesh just stared. He was frozen from the overpowering feeling of astonishment. "Triplets" was the thought that flashed into his head, and he would have smiled but didn't dare. He shuddered at the strange event happening before his very eyes.

Shortly Alesh's fright began to give way to a new feeling which warmed him. He suddenly felt like dashing to those strangers who seemed so amazingly related to him. But he did not, for he was still as rigid and unmoving as a sculpture chiselled from cold stone. Besides, he felt it was not becoming for a man of his years and position to childishly lose control of himself and his senses.

The strangers parted from their embrace and looked at one another lovingly.

"I have waited for you a long time, dear friend," said the first. In his soft brown eyes there burned the love of friendship. "This wait was long and full of hardship, but your return has brought joy and good fortune back to me. Now I will not let you go back to the outside world. You will stay here with me, and we will be together as we were before our life was split apart and we were sent in different directions."

The second stranger then suddenly grew cold and replied peevishly. "Do not deceive yourself. I didn't come back to stay. I'm going back to the outside world—back to the foreign country which has become my home—and you are going with me."

The first grew sad. "Stay by me," he begged, "for we are one, and it is not right that we should be kept apart any longer. Please stay!"

"I don't want to!" retorted the second, still peevish. "You are going with me! I cannot do without you any longer; besides, this separation has disturbed me. It has robbed me of my balance and has stolen my peace of mind. You're going with me, because your place is with me."

Now Alesh began to notice small differences between them. The eyes of the second stranger were harder and colder than those of the first. Still they appeared to be the eyes of a good and kind man. The first stranger spoke softly and melodiously. His voice murmured as a forest spring and whispered like a balmy breeze, while the other's voice was somewhat coarse. It came forth like the unpleasant echoes of the factory whistle, the jarring of locomotives, and the hissing, whining noise made by machines. Otherwise, the two remained as alike as two peas in a pod and in turn both were just as similar to Alesh himself.

Meanwhile, the first stranger cast a sad gaze on the second. "I can't go to that outside world, for I am tied to this land. This earth is like the bosom of my mother and I am chained here with a thousand ties. I am chained so strongly that no power on earth can tear me away from it. You stay here with me! This soil is our native land! This is our birthplace!"

"I cannot," replied the second and in his eyes there flashed a forlorn look. "I am also tied; although it is a foreign land, I have already become so accustomed to life there that it is like my own homeland. I cannot tear myself away. I think that it would be better if you would go with me; you should be with me as we were before that bitter hour of separation twenty years ago."

"I can't do it!"

"Nor can I! I am tied there."

Silence.

The two men bent their heads in sorrow. The tears began to run down their cheeks and fall upon the freshly plowed furrows in the rich brown earth.

"In vain!" said the second. He lifted his head and resignedly began to look around. "All these words are in vain because we will never be one, as we once were. Powerful unseen forces have split us in two. Each half knows its place and we will be tied to that place until death. I know it is terrible if one being is divided in two and then tied to two different continents separated by a surging endless sea. But we are unable to help ourselves. Try if you can! Try! Break the ties which chain me to that foreign country! Tie me here with such strong bonds that I cannot break them—not I, myself, nor any other power! We have fought with each other twenty years but all has been in vain. Shall we continue to fight in this fashion—entirely in vain and for no reason at all?" The first did not answer. He slowly turned his head toward the west and stared at the horizon above the snowcapped Julian Alps.

"Do you see, you are no longer able to tie me to this land. You neither dare nor do you believe that you can do it," the second softly murmured and across his face there passed the fleeting smile of bittersweet disappointment. "I would like to. . . ."

This was too much for Alesh. With great effort he tore himself from the spot where he had been rooted, and moved toward the two men.

"Tell me, who are you? You seem familiar and yet unfamiliar. I don't know whether you are old friends or only two strangers whom chance has brought across my path.

The strangers rose up at this, stepped toward him, and clung to him, one on each side. Alesh had both the feeling of being at ease with them and yet of great unease.

"Who are we? Your soul!"

"My soul?" In spite of everything, Alesh began to laugh aloud. "For heaven's sake, what's wrong with you? What is

Moses, by Lillian Brulc

churning in those heads of yours? Everyone knows that no man can have two souls."

"But we are one!" they pleaded.

"Please stop this nonsense!" And Alesh became angry indeed. "I am not blind and I see two individuals."

"Two halves," corrected the second and the first nodded in agreement. "Once we were one, but life split us in two. That was twenty years ago and since that time when we were split, we have continually argued with each other. Haven't you felt that there were two different opposing forces fighting for control of you all these years? Of course, the second almost had me in a corner. But now, once again, I have come to the fore and again my opinions will matter. You will feel my power and know my feelings, too!"

Alesh was amazed at this and he did not know whether he was awake or dreaming. "The devil take this affair! True, there were at times strange feelings I could not understand—as if there were something wrong with me, that something in me was quarreling, but. . . ."

"You see, that was us!" said the two strangers simultaneously, and at that moment they disappeared. They were nowhere to be seen.

Alesh felt terribly confused and unsettled at that moment. It was as if he had been split into two halves which were now bitterly quarreling between themselves. The beauty of his native valley, lovely at first sight a few moments ago, had lost much of its attraction for him. He suddenly had two powerful wishes, so opposite that they could not possibly survive together. The first wish was to return to his foreign home where he had lived the last twenty years. The second wish was to stay in his native land, here where he had been born and brought up. Alesh put his hands to his head.

"Damn, am I going crazy?" To convince himself that he was dreaming he bit his finger and the pain tore him from the power of sleep and his dreams.

Then he slept again and he dreamed wild dreams, dreams of the most fantastic images. His wife slept peacefully by his side. The panes of glass in the window rattled under the force of the wind, driving swarms of snowflakes before it. Alesh wiped the perspiration from his forehead and sighed in relief.

"Thank God, it was only a dream. But what a damn uncomfortable dream!"

And then he stepped to the window; by looking at the snow-covered streets of the American metropolis he wanted to convince himself it had been only a foolish dream. There were no strangers. In fact, there was no one to be seen. It had been only a dream. He had dreamed a strange foolish dream.

Only a foolish dream?

Alesh found a cigarette, lit it, and sat down to think. Last year he had been in the old country. He, himself, did not

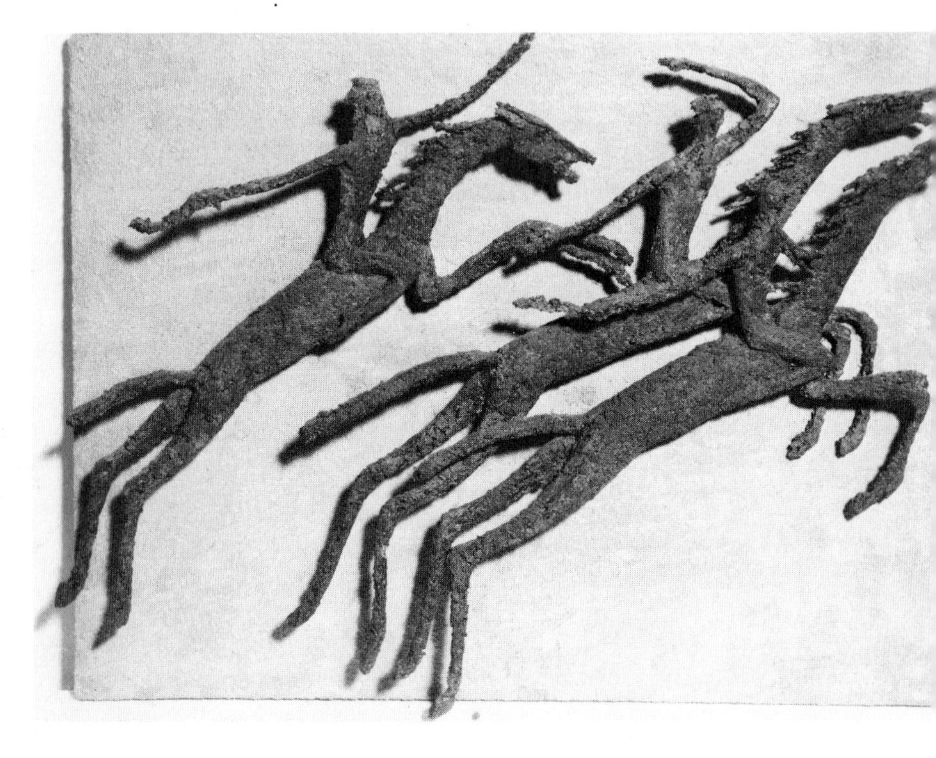

Apocalyptic riders, by France Gorše

know what had taken him there. He did know that since he had returned he had been somewhat disillusioned, almost ambivalent about life in general, and he did not know why. Was it because he had found something there? Something that unconsciously he had not hoped to find? What was it? Was it the violent separation of the two sides to his own soul?

Alesh blew a large puff of smoke against the windowpane and quietly murmured to himself. "The devil! They weren't so strange, those dreams. They weren't so strange as they seemed at first. Damn! There was truth in them! The splitting of a soul. . . ."

And Alesh's thoughts went back to the past, where they had travelled before.

John P. Nielsen (Šešek), by Božidar Jakac

John P. Nielsen

LETTER FROM NEW YORK

About a year ago in an extended stay in Cleveland I was visiting my cousin and we were discussing, oh, just anything I guess, when I mentioned I was going back to New York. My cousin asked me in a mild, to be sure, but definite are-you-all-right-in-the-head tone, "You're really going back to New York?"

Like the legendary man drowning, who sees his whole life flash by, I experienced a similar flashback going back fifty years, when I was still a teen-ager. We lived in Nottingham, as we called this particular Cleveland suburb, but as much as I liked the vineyardy surroundings of that day around our house, my feet were generally pointed in the direction of downtown. On many a day I hopped on a yellow streetcar and got off somewhere downtown. It took about an hour in those days. I usually stopped first in that wonderful Cleveland Public Library at Third and Superior. After drinking in the current literary magazines and browsing through a half a dozen science books, I went to a late lunch. In the arcade across the street, in the lower level, I got the best hamburg sandwich and piece of apple pie with cheddar cheese on the side. Then I would walk back past the Cleveland Plain Dealer building, then perhaps to the Cleveland Press offices, to smell the fresh-inked paper, and snatch the first copy of the evening edition sold just outside the premises. After that I might walk to the Hanna Theater hoping to see a celebrity going into the stage door. Finally, before going home, I would lounge a bit in one of the hotel lobbies, reading my newspaper, maybe pretending I was a hotel guest, but mostly trying to sense the aura of the big world outside of Cleveland.

All this was not good enough, and in due course, I headed for a more definite urban center—New York. I got there by train, checked into a "Y" and got myself a job in Bayonne, N.J., just across the river from Manhattan, requiring a daily commuting by subway and the Liberty Street ferry across the Hudson. I loved it. I particularly enjoyed, on occasion, seeing a big

SOURCE: *Ameriška Domovina*, 18 April 1975.

Metropolis, by H. Gregory Prusheck (Perušek)

liner go by the bow of the ferry in the mist of an early morning. I rented a room on Riverside Drive, in an apartment converted into a rooming house. Still not good enough, I found out in time. The Village was the place to live. And so, I drifted down there whenever I could to drool over the various houses that I hoped to live in someday. The couple of thousand dollars I saved up over three or four years wouldn't come near the fifteen thousand (those good old days) I needed for one of those houses on Washington Square. No. 5 on the Square, with its elaborate colonial doorway and with Boston ivy as a ground cover for the miniature lawn area, especially appealed to me. This house, my research told me, was none other than the one Henry James lived in back in 1850. Fifteen thousand for such a house! It didn't seem so much, so I decided to plan and wait.

Well, my aspirations for a distilled urban milieu were only an avocation. My serious occupation was as a chemist-metallurgist, and at that time I was pursuing a Ph.D. Finally I made it. Slow it came but come it did, through a series of fortunate circumstances. I spent the necessary four years in New Haven, a kind of far-removed New York suburb. And so back to Manhattan to join a university there.

I recall an incident on Times Square. I was squiring a girl when we came upon a skid row character leaning up against a building. His very black hair and other features told me that he was an American Indian; he was shouting to the passers-by, a bit incoherently, "Twenty-four dollars they gave us, a measly twenty-four dollars for Manhattan." Stupidly we laughed, thinking I suppose, "just another drunk." But that incident traced itself indelibly in my mind. It was not an act—there was no self-consciousness—it was the soul of an Indian cursing what the white man had done to him.

This absence of self-consciousness seemed to be characteristic of New York. The incident could not have happened in Arizona, or Utah. It took impersonal Times Square to give it the ring of truth. And tragic as the incident was, it fixed me more certainly in New York.

But I am groping for words. I don't really mean no self-consciousness, or the ring of truth. I think I mean a certain genuineness. In New York a cab driver looks and acts like a cab driver, through and through. In Akron or Albuquerque a cab driver is between jobs, or maybe waiting for his farm to be delivered to him, which he and his new bride purchased a month ago.

Mentioning a cab driver reminds me of the precious reply I got from one when I asked him if he knew where Sniffen Court was, as I hopped into his cab. "All I know is where's the Statue of Liberty." I had occasion recently to give a party at the Harvard Club for about twenty guests. One of the guests looking admiringly around the venerable establishment said that it was just what he expected the Harvard Club to look like.

Courtesy of News, Ltd.

Cathedral, by Stanislaus Rapotec

Yes, that's it—the real thing. A bar is a bar in New York, designed principally for dispensing alcoholic beverages. A cop is a professional cop. And that man in a top hat walking down the street gets no double takes. He has every right to wear it, not as a costume, but it belongs where it is, along with the decorations on his chest, as he enters one of the finer clubs on Fifth Avenue for a banquet at which some historical honor will be conferred on him.

Well, to make a long story short, I did make some money in the stock market, enough to buy one of those houses in the Village. Jimmy Walker's house, no less. Just think, as we were inspecting the house we found sheets of music scattered on the floor in a closet. One of the songs was the number Jimmy had composed, and, no doubt, Betty Compton, his wife, had sung: "Will You Love Me in December as You Do in May?" It was a handsome house—befitting a mayor of New York—on St. Luke's Place, one of the more elegant streets in the Village. I submitted my down payment. The owner I was dealing with was Jack Lawrence, composer of "Tenderly," "Ciri Biri Bin," and other hit songs. The lawyers wrangled over the deal, and in two months I lost out on the house and two thousand dollars in brokerage and lawyer fees in addition. However, I learned fast, and after shucking off the predatory lawyers, I made a down payment on an even more illustrious house on a Paris-like mews. Not only was it one of the choicest spots in New York, but the house I captured was the best in the mews. And what a mews! Cole Porter wrote his "Begin the Beguine" in the corner house, and fifteen years later, in the same house, Douglas wrote his best seller, *Lost Weekend*. The Lunts lived across the street. Melvina Hoffman, the celebrated sculptress, lived next door.

How could I miss? If ever I was to do creative work—this was the ambience. I was sure of it, especially when I read an article about writers in America, one Sunday morning in the book section of the *Times*, and the author of the piece speculated that no doubt somewhere a nineteen-year-old beast was inching his way across the country toward Manhattan to write his *The Sun Also Rises*.

The creativity did come, and the accompanying recognition and some prestige, enough for me to be listed in various *Who's Whos*. This, for my self-esteem, established me in my adopted community. Why does a big city like New York, Paris, or London help in the creativity expression? Hard to say, but it does. One thing I see here is dedication—a bit more than elsewhere—a dedication not for making money, or pushing one's family ahead as, say, in Texas, but simply for excellence.

I was at my local hardware store one day when Sam, the owner, called out to me, "Hey, Dr. Nielsen, you're a metallurgist, maybe one of the best in the country; I want to ask you a question about soldering." Well, I am not one of the

Steel and iron, by Stanko Tušek

best in the country, but I stand on it that I am one of the good ones. But my hardware man just automatically assumed I was one of the best. Well, that's New York. The dedicated professional, whether he be a photographer, a ballet dancer, a mathematician, or an authority on eggs, is found here, and if he is not the best in the country, then he is not very far from the best. Had my hardware man spoken to my neighbor, and wanted to ask about sculpturing, he would have had the opinion of a student of Rodin, and a world's authority in her own right. My wife once was puttering with some plantings around a tree in front of the house. A passerby stopped and gave some advice—good advice, it turned out. And why not? We learned later that she was only the gardening editor of the *New York Times*, who lived down the street a bit.

In a Fourth Avenue bookstore, while I was browsing over some old books, an old post card fell to the floor. The card, which had been mailed from France, was signed "E. Wharton." I took it to the Beinicke Rare Book Library at Yale to have the handwriting checked. Not only was the writing authentic, but I learned that the French town of Herres, on the Riviera, which was on the postmark, was where Edith Wharton had her chateau. I sent the card to her biographer, Louis Auchinclos, and we had a pleasant chat about it. I sensed that I was a part of history, at any rate American literary history, and I had encountered it in such a casual way. One just had to be in the mainstream of what is going on in the world.

"What was that you asked?" I said to my cousin. "Oh, yes, whether I am really going back to New York. Well," I answered, "you know how it is—it's the place I know best."

Frank Kerže (1876–1961)

Frank Kerže

PODBOY'S RETURN TO SLOVENIA

Translated by Florence Unetich

It was a cold, wintry morning when Mavro Podboy arrived in Ljubljana, where he spent a few hours purchasing clothing and other gifts to distribute among the villagers. Then he hired a coach and driver and drove off directly toward his native village. He stopped for the night in Velike Lašče. No one recognized him. Time had altered his appearance; the once boyish face was hidden under a man's beard. News of the rich American spread quickly, and soon, outside the house where he was staying, villagers lingered, hoping to catch a glimpse of him.

The next morning, rested, he started out on foot toward Mala Slevica. Before anything else, he had to find Franitsa, to see where and how she was. The pounding of his heart betrayed his anxiety as he trudged along the hilly road, pausing to catch a glimpse of his destination, Rašice, visible only from the tops of hillocks along the way.

It was already noon when he arrived at the modest little village and inquired for the home of Franitsa, the daughter of Krnec. A group of curious children gathered quickly, observing him silently, intently, but dashing away when he tried to question them. Only after he tossed a few coins among them, did they volunteer the answer he sought, and crowded about him, thrusting out grimy palms, pleading, "Me, too, uncle, me, too!"

They made a strange procession—he, the children, and a dog or two, such as generally escorted strangers through the village. The procession stopped finally on the other side of the village, before the second-last cottage. He motioned to the children who remained at a respectful distance while he walked through the open vestibule and peeped through the window of the door. At the table stood a woman. Though her face was not visible, he sensed it could only be she, his Franitsa. Blood rushed to his head. His heart beat rapidly; overcome with

SOURCE: Frank Kerže, "Za soncem," *Čas*, December, 1922, 358-59.

Slovenian village, by H. Gregory Prusheck (Perušek)

emotion, he restrained a wild desire to throw open the door and leap to her side. She was not yet aware of his presence as she gazed through the window, in mild wonder, at the children gathered in front of the house. Podboy tapped gently with his foot, then slowly opened the door. The woman turned toward the shadow-filled doorway in which only two glowing eyes were visible. A light burst upon her soul—"It is he!" She stared at the doorway, straining to see, to assure herself that it was indeed he and not a dream, not just a projection of her desire. Her legs seemed to move toward the door of their own accord; then she stopped a few paces away, unable to move further. Her hand reached up; she leaned against the wall and went limp. In a moment he was at her side, embracing her.

"Mavro, my Mavro!"

Slowly he inclined his head and brushed her forehead with his lips. The sorrow which had burdened her heart for so long lifted, as their eyes met in an embrace that washed away the pain of separation.

At twilight, there stood before the cottage the very best carriage the town could boast, all decorated with green boughs; the old mare harnessed to it tossed her head as proudly as if she were in the service of royalty.

The next day, Podboy went to the village tavern and ordered two kegs of wine from Urban, the tavernkeeper.

"Call all the villagers," he declared. "Today everyone is my guest and can drink his fill!"

Word spread like wildfire and villagers hurried to partake of his hospitality. Old Krnec hobbled in, stooped with age. Seeing his old adversary, Podboy stiffened momentarily. Then an inner voice whispered to him, "He is Franitsa's father!" Quietly, he walked over to the old man and extended his hand in greeting. Glass in hand, Krnec peered questioningly at Podboy and asked:

"Who are you, sir?"

"Don't you remember Podboy, father?"

The glass fell from the old man's nerveless fingers and shattered on the floor. Filled with compassion, Podboy took the old man's arm and led him to the table where he poured him another glass of wine.

"Podboy, Podboy," mused the old man, lost in thoughts of the past. His heart was heavy with remorse and had the earth swallowed him at that moment, he would have felt only relief.

"Drink, father, and be happy," said Podboy quietly. But Krnec seemed not to hear. Overcome with guilt and remorse, he wanted only to fling himself on his knees before Podboy and beg forgiveness. But everyone would see, and what would they think of old Krnec?

Podboy sensed the struggle raging in the old man and was moved to pity. After all, Krnec was Franitsa's father; why not let bygones be bygones? "Actually," mused Podboy, "I have only

Still life, by H. Gregory Prusheck (Perušek)

benefitted from his unpleasantness. Had Krnec been more agreeable, I would never have left, and would still be no more than his hired hand."

He leaned toward the old man and whispered, "Father Krnec, don't brood about the past. All is forgotten."

Gratefully, Krnec turned to him, searching his face for signs of forgiveness. Podboy's eyes assured him the words were sincere. He extended his hand and wrung Podboy's in gratitude.

* * *

Several years passed. Near the center of the town rose an imposing two-storied edifice, which even today, so many years later, remains one of the most attractive structures in the village. Its interior was tastefully furnished; the spacious family room contained fine, soft, easy chairs into which one sank comfortably. Evenings, Franitsa sat happily rocking their youngest child while the two older children listened to her recount tales of where their father had been and how he had worked to be able to provide them with such a luxurious home.

Podboy spent most of his time in another part of the building, where the sign on the door read "Mayor's Office." A steady stream of visitors came through his door daily. Some came seeking counsel, some help, and others came because of differences with neighbors. Wherever possible, Mayor Podboy assisted with counsel and sometimes with money. Late in the day, he would leave his desk, lock the door, and cross into the comfortable living quarters to relax. There he seated himself in an easy chair, lifted a child to each knee and sat contentedly rocking them. And if he stopped to rest a bit, the children shouted, "Giddap, horsey!" and his legs went into motion again.

After the children were asleep, Franitsa often asked:

"Mavro, tell me again how it was in Nevada. There were three of you, weren't there? Tell me about it."

Podboy laughed. He had already told her of his experiences so often that she knew each detail as well as he, yet she always begged to hear the story from the start. As he talked, she gazed into his face and she was so engrossed in reliving his experiences that sometimes she lost track of his words. When he finished, she wrapped her arms around his neck and asked trustingly:

"Tell me truthfully, Mavro; in all that time, did you never love another woman?"

"Never any other than you, my Franitsa."

"And you always thought about me?"

"Always and everywhere."

With that she would jump quickly to the table, turn down the lamp, and draw the red drapes at the window, and the room was in darkness. Only now and then a star peeked through some small chink around the windows, winked knowingly, and then hurried off to join her sister stars.

Marie Prisland, by Nancy Bukovnik

Marie Prisland

MEMORIES OF OUR OLD WOOD STOVE

Our children, much less our grandchildren, barely remember the old wood stove; but when fall brings its chilly winds, I often am warmed by the memory of our sturdy old wood range.

When I moved into our new home as a bride, the huge stove occupied the longest wall of our old-fashioned kitchen. The stove needed a lot of space because of its size and because of the hot water reservoir attached to it.

When I wanted a roaring fire, I would pull a metal bar in front of the stove and open the damper in the pipe. The stove crackled with glowing warmth. No modern stove could accomplish what the wood fire did.

In 1910 the iron range was a model of efficiency. With her polished black surface and nickel-plated trim, she was a beauty! Once a week she was given a dazzling shine with "Black Joe" stove polish. The nickel was washed with soap and water and then dried and polished.

We always had homemade bread, potica, pies, cookies, and coffee cake. There was no stove thermometer, but I knew by putting my hand into the oven whether it was exactly the right temperature for baking.

The range burned mostly wood but when winter came with near zero weather, we banked the fire with coal. The ashes were shaken carefully from the grates so that they fell into a narrow ash pan below. If the shakings were too vigorous, the grates dumped all their coals and then a new fire had to be started.

There were times when the warmth of the old stove was a great comfort. My son remembers having a bath as a child in the washtub in front of the open warm oven, and my daughters still recall the aroma of the red apples they placed on top of the hot stove to warm a little before they were eaten.

SOURCE: Marie Prisland, *From Slovenia to America* (Chicago: The Slovenian Women's Union of America, 1968), 167-68

Courtesy of Studia Slovenica

Dreams, by France Gorše

The children especially were fond of the old stove in winter. It warmed their cold and numb feet and dried their wet shoes and their soggy mittens which were hung behind the stove. One cold spring we brought our newly-hatched chickens into the kitchen. The mother hen watched over her brood, which was housed in a neat box beside the warm stove.

Yes, the old stove is gone, and gone with it is the tightly-knit family which gathered around the stove warming hands and hearts. . . .

Zdravko Novak (1909–1971)

Zdravko Novak

A PATCH OF EARTH

Translated by Joseph Kess

It's been a long time since I sat on those hard school benches and, for that reason, I have forgotten the measurements of the earth's size and circumference. But that really doesn't matter, for a man would be foolish to fill his head with empty and meaningless numbers. At any rate, one thing is certain—the globe is big enough! And God has made me a gift of a little patch of earth from this gigantic sphere that we inhabit.

It's sad that even this little patch isn't my native Slovenian soil. There's too little of it for everyone to walk away with some in his hand. Perhaps back home I didn't have as much land, not enough really to call my own, to stand on my own; nevertheless, I was at home, a native among natives, a friend among friends. Here I live on my own, self-supporting and independent, but I am like an exotic plant uprooted from the soil which bore me. I have never entirely taken and grown in the soil into which I was transplanted—maybe I never will. Even if a man does accustom himself to a foreign place, there comes a time when he is sharply, perhaps cruelly, reminded of the fact that he is, after all, a foreigner.

A little patch of earth! How happy indeed a man would be if it lay there, far away in his native land, the land that he calls home. Perhaps somewhere high up in Gorenjsko, with a magnificent view of Triglav; or perhaps along the torrent of the Sava, or beside a glittering lake, or on the edge of a forest along a murmuring brook; or perhaps somewhere in the green luxuriance of Štajersko, or along the fields of hops in the Sava valley, or near the hills planted with grapevines; or on the crest of a hill with its little white church, or along our lovely Slovenian Primorje.

A little patch of earth! Another strand of that thread of fate which tore us from our homeland and now links us even more

SOURCE: Zdravko Novak, "Tri pedi zemlje" (manuscript contributed for this anthology by Mrs. Milka Novak).

Longing, by Milan Vojsk

strongly to the foreign land. Thus are the ties with the homeland rent!

A little patch of earth! A little patch of foreign earth, and foreign though it is, I must confess that it has blessed us. True, a little patch is not very much, but it is enough for a home to stand on. Say the word to someone like me, who has roamed for thirty years or more—he will know what it means to have a home.

Behind the little house is a lawn and on it a tree. It is autumn. Perhaps that tree has stood there from the time when the first settlement was made on this land. It gives us pleasant shade so that the hot summer sun does not scorch us. I would indeed miss it if it were no longer there! At the end of the yard there is a small garden for vegetables and flowers. On that little fistful of land grow almost more vegetables than we can use.

When I am weary, my thoughts travel back to my native land. If only I could return there some day! How I would like to have a little patch of earth there! Since Slovenia is so small, I would even be satisfied if that patch of earth were less than my plot here, where there is more than enough land for all. How pleasant it would be if I might find my final home there, in my native land, where I could rest and catch my breath from all the burdens which life in the new country has heaped upon me. How fortunate I would be if my wish were fulfilled!*

---

*This is Novak's last "short story," written shortly before his death from cancer in 1971, in Cleveland, Ohio.

Anna Krasna

Anna Krasna

WINGS IN THE CLOUDS

There was nothing in the gloominess of the day to dispel the feelings that weighed on the soul like so much lead. For hours now father lay still, his eyes closed to the world, his breath growing fainter and fainter. His toilworn hands were yet flexible, but cold . . . and somehow, Mila knew they'd never be warm again . . . and, somehow, she managed to stand by and wait . . . without tears. All alone with a dying man who was her father . . . whose hands, strong and loving, used to lift her almost sky-high when the glorious sun of childhood shone all over the courtyard, over the wide valley itself, and the faraway world beyond the hills and mountains. All was cloudy now. The valley narrowed into the shape of a grave . . . horizons of faraway worlds were curtained off . . . up in the thick layers of gray moisture circled man-propelled wings, as though trying to find a way out of dark, dark clouds.

Wings swished and whirled, the sound reaching in through the open windows, suddenly wakening already subsiding fears of the dying man—

—T-i-m-b-e-r—

—No, father. No timber is falling—that's wings, father . . . friendly wings, not the enemy's.

"W-i-n-g-s—" He tried to open his eyes to see; he couldn't. Mila looked at the clock and wondered if the priest would come soon—and wondered at the same time why he should come . . . what was the use? Why didn't she keep the children with her instead of sending them out after relatives and the priest? Why should they come now—no one came last night. She shivered at the thought of the night just passed . . . of the delirious attempts of her father to escape falling timber . . . his strength . . . his eyes staring, yet seeing nothing . . . his hands reaching out to avoid timber . . . his body springing out of bed only to collapse . . . and outside—the black storm rag-

---

SOURCE: Anna Praček Krasna, *Za lepše dni* (New York: Samozaložba, 1950), 114-15.

The Martyr, by H. Gregory Prusheck (Perušek)

ing, cutting off all the world, isolating them, and ripping their young hearts with stabbing fears.

But now everything was calm. There was no more fear, no hysterical pain in the brain, not even desire for tears—only deep, deep sorrow, surrounded with the beauty of all the memories of one who had a kind and noble heart and was now going away . . . to the tune of wings, circling and cutting through grey layers as though trying to find a way out of dark, dark clouds. . . .

The immigrant, by Ted Kramolc

V

SLOVENIAN AMERICAN LITERATURE

Baraga

Trunk

Buh

Zakrajsek

Rausch

Kristan

Molek

Zupancic

Krasna

Zavertnik

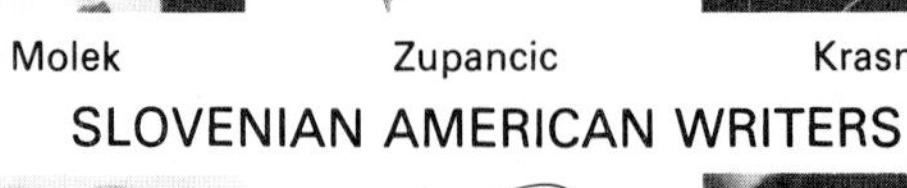

SLOVENIAN AMERICAN WRITERS

Adamic

Zorman

Mauser

Mlakar

Jontez

Nielsen

Kern

Prisland

Zaitz

Klancar

Rogelj

Kobal

Zaplotnik

Novak

Grill

Giles Edward Gobetz

SLOVENIAN AMERICAN LITERATURE

Background Information

The Slovenians, or the Slovenes, are the westernmost Slavic people who currently number a little over 1,800,000 in their native land, Slovenia, the northernmost republic of Yugoslavia, and close to a million, including about 500,000 in the United States, in all other countries. Because of their small numbers and centuries of political subjugation, they have been relatively little known in America and the world.[1] Who, then, are the Slovenians and what are some of their historic and cultural characteristics which may have influenced their literature in the New World?

According to Bernard Newman, the noted English author,

> . . . Slovenia's masters ranged from Charlemagne to Napoleon, but the people clung tenaciously to their own culture and language. . . . The Slovenes used to share with the Scandinavians the reputation of being the best-read people in the world—the number of books read per head of the population was four times the British figure. . . . It was manifestly impossible for a small people to gain and hold its freedom when surrounded by acquisitive great powers, but the Slovenes, determined to secure the greatest possible degree of home rule, concentrated on cultural rather than on political liberty. It was a miracle of survival almost without parallel. The boundaries of Slovenia have never been based on physical features; they rest upon the moral strength of its people.[2]

In De Bray's *Guide to the Slavonic Languages* we read that "literacy in Slovenia reaches almost a hundred percent and their beautiful literature is often characterized by a gentle melancholy or a positive and constructive optimism."[3] Louis

---

Reprinted and revised, by permission, from Giles Edward Gobetz, "Slovenian Ethnic Literature," published in *Ethnic Literatures Since 1776: The Many Voices of America*, ed. W. T. Zyla and W. M. Aycock, Proceedings of the Comparative Literature Symposium, vol. 9, part 2 (Lubbock: Texas Tech University Press, 1976).

Glagolite ponas redka zlouesa
Bose gospodi milostiuvi. otze bose tebe izpovuedo
vues moi greh. i zuetemu crestu. i zuetei marii. i zue
temu michaelu. i uuzem crilatcem bosiem. i zuetemu pe
tru. i usem zelom bosiem. i usem musenicom bosiem.
usem vuernicom bosiem. i usem devuam praudnim. i use
praudnim. i tebe bosi rabe chocu biti izpovueden. u sech moih
greh. i vueru iu. da mi ie na sem zuete bousi. iti se na on
suet. pakise ubrati. na sod zodni. i meti mi iesi vuot
posem. i me ti mi ie ot pustene moih grechou. Bose
milostiuvi. primi moiu izpovued. moih grechou. ese
iesem ztuoril zla. pot den pongese bih na si zvuet
vuuraken. ibih crisken. ese pomngu. ili ne pomngu.
vuolu. ili ne vuolu. ili vuede. ili ne vuede. ili u ne praud
nei rote. ili ulsi. ili tatbe. ili zavuisti. ili v ulinabi.
ili v sminstue. ili ese mi se tomu ubo se lo ... mibi ne dos
talo choteti. ili v proglagolani. ili spe ... ne zpe. ili ese
iesem ne zpasal nedela. ni zueta vuecera. ni mega
potra. i inoga mnoga. ese protiu bogu. i protiu me
mu crestu. Ti edin bose vuez. eaco mi iega potre
ba vuelica. Bose gospodi milostivi. tebe ze mil
tuoriu. od sih posteníh grech. i odineh mnozeh.
i vuensih. i minsih. ese iesem ztvoriL. tebe
miltuoriu. i suetei marii. i u sem svetim.

Courtesy of Dr. Rudolf Trofenik Verlag, Munich, Germany

Facsimile of a page of the Freising Leaves or *Brižinski spomeniki*, one of the oldest documents written in Slovenian and in any Slavic language, believed to date from around 1,000 A.D.

Adamic tells us that in Slovenia "most of the streets are named after poets, essayists, novelists, dramatists, and grammarians"[4] and R. H. Markham, an American author who spent some time in Slovenia, compares the coffee houses in Slovenian cities with the reading rooms in American public libraries.[5]

In their millenium-long struggle for survival as a distinct nationality group the Slovenians have concentrated on their Slovenian language and, since the early days of the Protestant Reformation, on their literature as the crucially important vehicles of their national consciousness and culture and their primary means of survival as a distinct people. This situation gave the Slovenian *literati* a somewhat disproportionally important position in Slovenian society. This same orientation has, to a great extent, been transplanted to America, especially among Slovenian-born immigrants.[6]

Among other factors which have played an important role in the Slovenian national consciousness and prestige is the early democracy which flourished in their northernmost province of Carinthia many centuries before the world-famous Magna Carta of 1215 came into being. This ancient Slovenian democracy and the ritual of the installation of the dukes of Carinthia were described in superlative terms by many famous historians and philosophers, among then Aeneas Silvius Piccolomini (who later became Pope Pius II) and Jean Bodin, whose book, *Les six livres de la Republique*, published in 1576, has frequently been considered the greatest work in political science since Aristotle's *Politics*.[7] According to this ritual, described by Piccolomini as "something unique and unheard of in other lands" and by Bodin as being "without equal in the world," the newly elected Duke of Carinthia was installed and recognized as the ruler of this northernmost region of Slovenia only after he had publicly and solemnly promised his electors and subsequent subjects that he would be a good judge, a just and courageous protector of his country, and a compassionate supporter of widows and orphans.[8]

As Professor Felicijan points out, Bodin's book was read by Thomas Jefferson, who initialed the description of the ancient Slovenian Carinthian democracy. The democratic ritual which was practiced in Carinthia between the seventh and early fifteenth centuries represented an early concrete historical precedent for the social contract theory—*the* theory which provided the ideological, legal, and moral justification for the American Declaration of Independence and subsequent revolution. Since Jefferson initialed a text and made marginal notations only when he considered it to be of exceptional significance, Professor Felicijan maintains that Jefferson singled out this democratic Slovenian ritual as a historical precedent of the social contract theory and as one of the important elements on which the Declaration of Independence was based.[9]

Slovenian poet France Prešeren (1800–1849), by Milan Vojsk

On the other extreme is a conservative evaluation by the Harvard historian Crane Brinton, who concedes to Slovenians a minor, but a real role in the development of our Western democratic institutions. In Brinton's opinion,

> . . . the picturesque Slovenian ceremony was reasonably well known to political philosophers, and indeed through Bodin known to Thomas Jefferson. This Slovenian ceremony was a part of a complex tradition, a minor variable but a real one, in the cluster of ideas that . . . went into the making of modern Western democratic institutions.[10]

Another founding father of our nation, Benjamin Franklin, was also somewhat dependent on a modest Slovenian writer, grammarian, and translator, Janez (in Slovenian), Johann (in German), or John (in English) Primec (or Primic), who not only discussed Franklin in Slovenian, but also translated him into German, and thus helped to popularize the thought of this wisest American in several European countries in the early years of the United States of America.[11]

Similarly, a number of prominent American writers and poets heard and recorded the voice of Slovenia, among them Henry Wadsworth Longfellow, whose *Hyperion: A Romance* includes "The Story of Brother Bernardus," based on the life and works of the Slovenian American immigrant writer and scholar, Bernard Smolnikar, who advocated a universal church, a world government, and universal peace and justice before, during, and after the American Civil War. His works in English and German have been preserved at Harvard University and other leading centers of learning.[12]

From these few examples it is clear that despite the vast differences in size and political condition between the United States and Slovenia, the common hunger for freedom and progress sparked a cross-fertilization of ideas between the two countries. As the bearers of this heritage, who are the Slovenian writers and poets who lived and worked in America and what is their role in American literature and culture?

Overview of Slovenian American Literature

The first contributions made by Slovenian American writers consisted of travel reports and ethnographic works. The earliest such writings known to us are those of Mark Anton Kappus (1657-1717), a Slovenian missionary, explorer, professor, and rector of the College of Matapé, and one of the three principal trailblazers involved in *Viages a la Nacion Pima en California* (Travels to the Nation of Pima in California) in 1694. Kappus also authored *Enthusiasmus sive solemnes ludi poetici* (Enthusiasm, or Solemn Poetical Plays, 1708), consisting of 276 chronograms and representing an early attempt in America at combining poetry, history, and ethnography.[13] (Kappus was, according to Professor Bolton and other authorities, also the first person

Slovenian writer Ivan Cankar (1876–1919), by H. Gregory Prusheck (Perušek)

who, in 1701, sent to Europe the very first geographic map which informed the world that California was not an island, as it had been believed until then, but a solid part of the American mainland.[14])

The next most famous Slovenian American ethnographic work is a book about the American Indians written by the Slovenian immigrant missionary and the first Bishop of Marquette, Frederic Baraga (1797-1868). This book was first published in 1837 in simultaneous German, French, and Slovenian editions.[15] It was followed by a similar work on the Indians of North America, *Die Indianer in Nord Amerika*, authored in German by the Slovenian missionary, Franc Pirc (or Franz Pierz, 1785-1880), and published in St. Louis in 1855.

Travel and ethnographic reports, published in books and in Slovenian, American, Austrian, and other magazines, journals, and newspapers, continued throughout the nineteenth and twentieth centuries, ranging from Baraga and Pirc to our contemporaries Joseph Grdina,[16] Dr. Andrew Kobal,[17] and Jim Klobuchar.[18]

The modern Slovenian American culmination of this genre of literature was reached with *The Native's Return*, by the Slovenian immigrant author Louis Adamic (1899-1951).[19] Chosen the Book-of-the-Month Club selection for February of 1934, it became an instant success and transformed Adamic into a national celebrity.[20] Adamic thus, for the first time, presented a glimpse of Slovenia to the larger American reading public.

As might be expected, Slovenian literary traditions transplanted to America by the Slovenian-born *literati* have exerted a strong influence on their work. In addition to the high value placed on literature and the leading status awarded by Slovenian society to its writers and poets, Slovenia has also been characterized by an unusually pronounced emphasis on ideological distinctions among the various "camps" or "schools." Conservative Catholicism and innovative liberalism have been the strongest ideological subdivisions in Slovenian literature, as well as in economics, politics, and several other aspects of Slovenian national life. This strongly marked ideological continuum, which ranges from religious and Catholic-inspired literature on the one extreme, through relatively "neutral" writings to progressive (liberal), socialist, and radical orientations at the opposite end of the scale, has also characterized Slovenian American ethnic literature, particularly that of the Slovenian-born *literati*.[21]

Among the oldest and perhaps the most persistent of these ideologically based categories is Slovenian Catholic religious literature, whose first and most prolific Slovenian American representative was Bishop Frederic Baraga (1797-1868). During his busy American career as missionary, bishop, and scholar (1831-1868), Baraga authored a large volume of meditations, several prayer books, epistles, and pastoral letters in the

Frederic Baraga (1797–1868), Slovenian American bishop and scholar

Otchipwe (Ojibway) and Ottawa Indian dialects, and in the Slovenian, German, and French languages.[22]

Several generations of Slovenian American missionaries and priests, nuns and laymen continued to contribute to this genre of literature up to the present time, among them: Kazimir Zakrajšek, O.F.M. (1878-1958), with his many prayer books, meditations, and religious booklets and articles;[23] Bishop Gregory Rožman (1883-1959), whose serialized spiritual thoughts and articles appeared in many Slovenian Catholic magazines, almanacs, and newspapers;[24] and our contemporaries, Joseph Vovk, best known for his translations into Slovenian of religious poetry, psalms, and hymns;[25] Joann Birsa, Edward Krasovich, Valentine Spendov, O.F.M., Dr. Alfred Fischinger, Frank Perkovich, and many others who have helped to popularize Slovenian religious songs (often in English translation) and music in America;[26] and Fortunat Zorman, O.F.M., current editor of the Slovenian language *Ave Maria* magazine and of an annual almanac of the same name, published by the Slovenian Franciscan Fathers of Lemont, Illinois.[27]

Among the noteworthy contributions to Slovenian American religious literature one should also mention such works as John C. Gruden's *The Mystical Christ*, published in London, England, and St. Louis, Missouri, in 1936; George Trunk's translation from Slovenian into English of France Veber's theodicy text, *There Is a God* (1942); Anthony Merkun's ecumenical work, *Cirilmetodijska ideja* (The Cyril-Methodian Idea, 1952); and Charles Wolbang's continuous series on the Slovenian Catholic missions throughout the world, published in *Ameriška Domovina*, a Cleveland-based Slovenian daily newspaper.[28]

Although nearly all of the approximately 500,000 Slovenians now living in the United States are Catholic (practical or nominal, as the case may be), Slovenian Americans have also contributed to non-Catholic religious literature in America. Thus, Andreas Bernardus Smolnikar (1795-1869), a Slovenian immigrant who had started his career as a Catholic priest and theologian, later became an ardent anti-Catholic religious reformer. Smolnikar spread his ideas not only through his oratory at numerous American religious and civic affairs and in conferences with American political and civic leaders, but also as a prolific writer of works advocating a universal religion and world government with universal justice and peace, the emancipation of women and slaves, and utopian socialism. The author of at least seven books, Smolnikar was a blend of brilliance and eccentricity, the founder of several millenial communities, and a very colorful personality. He was the subject of several literary essays, including one by Longfellow,[29] and was referred to, probably half-seriously and half-jokingly, as the "thirteenth apostle."[30]

A century after Smolnikar, Dr. Joseph L. Mihelic, a Slovenian American professor of the Old Testament, Literature, and

Languages at Dubuque Theological Seminary, gained distinction as a Presbyterian theologian and writer who, in addition to other works, contributed over forty articles to the *Interpreter's Bible Dictionary* and the *Encyclopedia Britannica.*[31]

The Slovenian religious writers are followed on the ideological continuum by those Catholic *literati* who dealt with secular themes from a Catholic point of view or who wrote under the Catholic label. Only a few leading names of the several scores of these Catholic Slovenian American writers and poets can be mentioned here, among them the following missionaries and priests: Oton Skola, O.F.M. (1805-1879), a talented writer, poet, and painter; Ivan Čebul (1832-1898), author of essays, articles, and poems in Slovenian, English, French, Greek, and Indian languages; Msgr. Joseph Buh (1833-1922), founder and vicar general of the Diocese of Duluth, writer and editor of *Amerikanski Slovenec* (The American Slovenian); Simon Lampe, O.S.B. (1865-1939), writer, educator, and an authority on the Otchipwe language; Antoine Rezek (1867-1946), writer and historian, best known for his two-volume *History of the Diocese of Sault Ste. Marie and Marquette* (1906, 1907); George Trunk (1870-1973), writer, historian, translator, and painter (at the time of his death, the oldest Catholic priest in America); Andrew Smrekar (1871-1939), poet, writer, and a prolific translator who, among other works, translated Shakespeare into Slovenian; Hugo Bren, O.F.M. (1881-1953), theologian, writer, translator, and editor; Kazimir Zakrajšek, O.F.M. (1878-1958), author of numerous short stories, novelettes, dramas, and plays, and founder and editor of *Ave Maria* monthly magazine and annual almanac; John Oman (1879-1966), contributor to Catholic Slovenian American magazines and newspapers; Bernard Ambrožič, O.F.M. (1892-1973), editor and author of numerous short stories and novelettes; Alexander Urankar, O.F.M. (1902-1952), poet; Vital Vodušek (1906-1973), best known for his collections of poems, *Pesmi* (Poems, 1928) and *Poezije* (Poetry, 1937); and Edward Surtz, S.J. (1909-1973), writer, scholar, literary critic, and an internationally known authority on St. Thomas More.[32]

Among living Slovenian American Catholic priests and nuns (1977), the following authors of secular works from the Catholic point of view stand out: Msgr. John L. Zaplotnik, the most prolific biographer of Slovenian American missionaries and contributor to numerous Slovenian and American magazines, journals, almanacs, and newspapers;[33] Basil Valentin, O.F.M., former editor of *Ave Maria* in America and current editor of *Misli* (The Thoughts) in Australia, a novelist, story teller, children's author, and poet;[34] William Furlan, best known for his book *In Charity Unfeigned* (1952); Bishop James S. Rausch (Slovenian on his mother's side), general secretary of the National Conference of Catholic Bishops and of the United States Catholic Conference, author and editor of influential works on human rights, the Catholic Church, American society, and international affairs;[35] Sisters Bernard Coleman and Verona LaBud, authors of *Masinaigans: The Little Book* (1972); and Sister Lavoslava Turk, contributor to Catholic magazines and papers and author of *Pesem šolske sestre* (The Song of a School Sister), a collection of short stories, published in 1974.

Among laymen, several Slovenian American writers and poets have been classified as Catholic authors. Included in this category are: Anton Klinc (1862-1949), writer and editor of *Narodna Beseda* (Our Nation's Voice) and *Nova Domovina* (New Homeland); James Debevec (1887-1952), humorist, writer, and editor of *Sloga* (Harmony), *Glas SDZ* (Voice of SDZ), and *Ameriška Domovina* (American Home); Louis Pirc (1888-1939), writer and editor of *Nova Domovina* and *Ameriška Domovina*; Ivan Zupan (1875-1950), editor of *Glasilo KSKJ* (The KSKJ Herald) and poet, best known for his collection of poems *Iz življenja za življenje* (From Life for Life, 1935); John Jerich (1894-1973), editor of *Amerikanski Slovenec* (The American Slovenian), *Baragova Pratika* (Baraga's Almanac), and *Novi Svet* (The New World), and author of numerous essays, articles, and a collection of short stories;[36] Zdravko Novak (1909-1971), author of such novels as *Pota božja* (God's Ways, 1957) and *Utrinki* (Fragments, 1959), of several dramatizations, and of over two hundred short stories and articles; and Fred Orehek (1922-1976), editorial writer for *The Chicago Tribune* and author of several short stories and biographies of Slovenian Americans.[37]

The most prolific contemporary Slovenian American Catholic writer and poet is Karl Mauser (1918-1977), who came to America in 1950 as a refugee and has gained international recognition as author of over twenty novels, several dramas, and a large number of novelettes which were published by various publishers in Europe and both Americas. Many of his beautiful short stories and poems have also appeared in Slovenian magazines, almanacs, and newspapers in the United States, Canada, Argentina, Austria, and Australia.[38]

Among the living Slovenian American Catholic *literati* the following names stand out: Stanley Zupan, former English editor of *Glasilo KSKJ*, of *Marquette News*, and of *Skyline*, the literary quarterly of Cleveland College, a talented author of short stories and essays; Ivan Račič, former editor of *Amerikanski Slovenec*, writer, and musician; Marie Prisland, writer and columnist, known for her book of "collections and recollections," *From Slovenia to America*, published in 1968; Professor Frank Bukvich, storyteller and novelist, best known for his novel *Brezdomci* (The Homeless, 1948), a penetrating analysis of the uprooted victims of war; Dr. Ludvik Puš, author of two books of memoirs, including *Klasje v viharju* (Harvest in the Tempest, 1970); Mirko Javornik, a talented neo-realist whose most important literary works were published prior to his immigration to America in the 1950's; Gizella Hozian, a newspaper columnist known also for her book *Spomini mladosti* (Reminis-

Major Slovenian American periodicals and newspapers, in 1921

cences of Youth, 1961); and Milena Soukal, Rose Mary Prosen, Marian Jakopic, and Eric Kovačič, poets.[39]

Closer to the "middle range" or "neutral" orientation of the ideological continuum we find, in addition to hundreds of Slovenian American authors in such fields as science, education, medicine, and related areas, also several Slovenian American *literati*, among them: Frank Sakser (1876-1961), writer and essayist and editor of *Glas Naroda* (The People's Voice) and of *Slovensko-Amerikanski Koledar* (Slovenian American Almanac); Frank Kerže (1876-1961), author of many novelettes, essays, short stories, and poems, and editor of the humor magazine *Komar* (Mosquito), of *Glasilo SNPJ* (The SNPJ Herald), and of the literary magazine *Čas* (Time); Anton Terbovec (1882-1962), humorist, essayist, storyteller, and editor of *Nova Doba* (New Era); Dr. Frank J. Kern (1887-), editor of *Glasnik* (The Herald) and *Clevelandska Amerika* (Cleveland's America), and author of an English-Slovenian dictionary (*Angleško-slovenski besednjak*, 1919), of an English-Slovenian reader (*Angleško-slovensko berilo*, 1926), of many articles on health and medicine, and of a very valuable book of memoirs, *Spomini*, published in 1937; and Ivan Zorman (1889-1957), composer and the leading Slovenian American poet, widely known among Slovenians for his collections *Poezije* (Poetry, 1919), *Pesmi* (Poems, 1922), *Lirični spevi* (Lyric Poems, 1925), *Slovene Poetry* (1928), *Pota ljubezni* (The Pathways of Love, 1931), and *Iz novega sveta* (From the New World, 1938).[40]

Others in this category are: Janko Rogelj (1895-1974), editor of *Enakopravnost* (Equality) and author of numerous articles, essays, and poems, including three collections of short stories and poems; Vatro Grill (1899-1976), editor of *Enakopravnost*, columnist, translator, and author of a book of memoirs, *Med dvema svetovoma* (Between Two Worlds, 1977); Dr. Andrew Kobal (1899-), who, in addition to his many scientific works, authored two books on his world-wide travels, numerous short stories and essays, and fifteen dramas; Ivan Jontez (1902-), editor of the literary magazine *Cankarjev Glasnik* (Cankar's Herald) and a talented novelist, storyteller, and poet, best known for his books *Senca preko pota* (A Shadow Across My Path, 1940), *Jutro brez sonca* (Morning without Sun, 1949), and *Trouble on East Green Street* (1956); Dr. Oton Ambrož (1905-), a highly regarded journalist, essayist, and scholar, especially acclaimed for his two-volume book, *Realignment of World Power* (1972); Anthony J. Klančar (1908-), essayist, translator, scholar, and journalist; Frank Mlakar (1913-1967), an exceptionally gifted storyteller, poet, and novelist whose book, *He, the Father* (1950), transformed him into a nationally known writer; Ben Kocivar (1916-), former senior editor of *Look* magazine, writer, and commentator; Robert Debevec (1918-), a talented author of short stories and articles, as well as of two legal books; William Horvat (1919-), former editor of *Journal of*

Louis Adamic, Slovenian American writer and social critic, by Nancy Bukovnik

American Aviation Historical Society, widely known for his book *Above the Pacific* (1966); and Professor Bernard Jerman (1921-). scholar, biographer, and literary critic, best known in America and England for his book, *The Young Disraeli* (1960).[41]

A more comprehensive overview should also discuss the role of such writers, poets, essayists, editors, reporters, critics, commentators, and/or translators of various ideological orientations as: Joseph Ambrožič, Heinie Martin Antoncic, John Arnez, Ivan Avsenek, Paul Borstnik, Mary Bostian, Mary Cassidy, Jim Debevec, Frank Dolence, Robert Dolgan, Josephine Erjavec, Joseph Felicijan, Anthony Garbas, Milena Gobetz, John and Julia Gottlieb, Joseph Gregorich, Janez Grum, William Heiliger, Jacob Hocevar, Toussaint Hocevar, Frances Jazbec, Joseph and Louis Jerkic, Richard Juvancic, Ivan and Jennie Kapel, Joseph Kess, Victor Knaus, Frank Kolaric, Miha Krek, Vincent Lauter, Rado Lencek, Lud and Corrine Leskovar, Vinko Lipovec, Joseph Melaher, James Mally, Albina Novak, Bogdan Novak, Irene Odorizzi, Anton Okolish, Tony Petkovsek, Josephine Petric, Julia Pirc, Ludwig Potokar, Edwin Primoshich, Jacob Resnik, Anton Sabec, Janez Sever, Antoinette Simcic, Mary Skerlong, Frank Sodnikar, Rado Staut, Frank Suhadolnik, Rick Sustaric, Matt Tekavec, Andrew and Agnes Tomec, Frank and Antonia Turek, Florence Unetich, Joseph Valencic, Joseph Velikonja, Mary Volk, Bogomil Vošnjak, Cyril Zebot, and, especially, Joseph Zelle, writer and translator; Dr. John P. Nielsen (Šešek), storyteller, essayist, and former editor of *Metallurgy/Materials Education Yearbook*; Louis Ule, an authority on the works of Marlowe and Shakespeare, literary critic, and co-inventor of the world's first electronically valved automobile engine; Elsie Rudman, writer and historian; Nada Skerly, former *Time* magazine reporter and an award-winning writer on the aged; Elaine Cimperman Slater, a free-lance writer for several American magazines; Stanley Modic, current executive editor of *Business Week* and former editor of *Our Voice*; Margot Klima, editor of *Our Voice* and of the *Clevelander* magazine; John Kameen, writer and publisher of the *Forest City News*; and Veda Ponikvar, writer and editor of the *Free Press* and *The Tribune Press*.[42]

Many works of Louis Adamic (1899-1951) are ideologically "neutral" (i.e., neither rightist nor leftist, neither pro-Catholic nor pro-socialist), while some of his books have been classified as progressive, socialist, or leftist, depending on the values and orientations of groups or persons who provided the label. Adamic, who came to America at the age of fifteen, has become the best known Slovenian American writer. Professor Henry A. Christian has compiled an impressive but, inevitably, incomplete list of 564 titles authored by Adamic, including books, pamphlets, articles, forewords, and other contributions. Christian also lists over five hundred items by other American and European authors, dealing with the life and works of Louis Adamic.

Among Adamic's most important works are the following books: *Dynamite: The Story of Class Violence in America* (1931), *Laughing in the Jungle: The Autobiography of an Immigrant in America* (1932), *The Native's Return: An American Immigrant Visits Yugoslavia and Discovers His Old Country* (1934), *Grandsons: The Story of American Lives* (1935), *Cradle of Life: The Story of One Man's Beginnings* (1936), *The House of Antigua: A Restoration* (1937), *My America: 1928-1938* (1938), *From Many Lands* (1940), *Two-Way Passage* (1941), *What's Your Name?* (1942), *My Native Land* (1943), *A Nation of Nations* (1945), *Dinner at the White House* (1946), and *Eagle and the Roots* (1952). Adamic was also editor of *Common Ground* and of the *Peoples of America Series*. A master of prose and a very influential popular historian, sociologist, social philosopher, critic, and reformer, he gained national and international fame, as well as criticism and hostility which ultimately cost him his life.[43]

In our present overview, Adamic can be considered the transition from the "neutral," "middle range" orientation to the progressive and socialist camps—a somewhat ambiguous position which he shares with a number of other authors, such as Kerže, Grill, Rogelj, and Jontez. The leaders of the progressive and socialist camps (the two labels have often been used interchangeably) were: Etbin Kristan (1867-1953), editor of *Svoboda* (Freedom), *Rdeči Prapor* (Red Standard), and *Zarja*(The Dawn) in Europe, and of *Ameriški Družinski Koledar* (American Family Almanac), *Proletarec* (The Proletarian), and *Cankarjev Glasnik* (Cankar's Herald) in America, and author of many volumes of poems, short stories, dramas, novels, and novelettes;[44] Joseph Zavertnik (1896-1929), editor of *Glas Svobode* (The Voice of Freedom), *Proletarec, Glasilo SNPJ, Slovenski Delavski Koledar* (Slovenian Workers' Almanac), and *Prosveta* (Enlightenment), best known for his comprehensive volume *Ameriški Slovenci* (American Slovenians, 1925); Martin Konda (1872-1922) and Frank Medica (1875-1955), editors of *Glas Svobode* and *Mir* (Peace);[45] Ivan Molek (1882-1962), editor of *Glasnik* (Herald) and *Prosveta*, storyteller, translator, and author of *Dva svetova* (Two Worlds, 1932), *Veliko mravljišče* (The Huge Anthill, 1934), and *Sesuti stolp* (The Tower That Collapsed, 1935);[46] Frank Zaitz (1888-1967), editor of *Ameriški Družinski Koledar, Majski Glas* (The Voice of May), and *Proletarec*, and a prolific author of essays, short stories, and articles about Slovenian Americans;[47] Frank Magajna (1895-1971), novelist, satirist, and translator into Slovenian from English and French;[48] Katka Zupančič (1889-1967), who authored over three hundred poems, five dramas, and 137 short stories and articles;[49] Jack Tomsic (1897-), a worker-poet whose poems were published in various progressive magazines and papers and appeared in a collection, *Pognale so na tujih tleh* (They've Grown in a Foreign Land, 1968); and Anna

Krasna (1900-), former editor of *Glas Naroda*, translator, and author of numerous short stories, novelettes, and poems, including a collection of poems, *Za lepše dni* (For a Better Future, 1950).[50]

Many authors of progressive-socialist orientation also contributed their short stories, novelettes, poems, and articles to *Ameriški Družinski Koledar* (American Family Almanac, 1915-1950), *Majski Glas* (The Voice of May, 1933-1945), *Cankarjev Glasnik* (Cankar's Herald, 1937-1943), and *Mladinski List* (The Voice of Youth, 1922-), and to other progressive publications, such as *Proletarec*, *Prosveta*, *Rodna Gruda*, and *Slovenski Izseljenski Koledar*. In addition to Kristan, Zavertnik, Molek, Zaitz, Katka Zupancic, and Krasna, and to such popular historians, storytellers, and critics as Frank Česen and Louis Kaferle, the following major contributors to various progressive publications should be mentioned: Frank Alesh, Louis Beniger, Vincent Caikar, Angelo Cerkvenik, Josip Chesarek, Josip Durn, Peter Elish, Slavica Fisher, Anton Garden, Filip and Oscar Godina, Erazem Gorshe, Mary Grill-Ivanusch, Louis and Louisa Jartz, Joseph Jauh, William Jereb, Mary Kobal, Mirko Kuhel, Donald Lotrich, Ludwig and Milan Medvesek, Zdenka Mihelich, Mary Jug-Molek, Zvonko Novak, Joško Oven, Matt Petrovich, John Pollock, Leo Poljšak, Betty Rotar, Doris Sadar, Louis Serjak, Anton Shular, Joseph Sircel, Joseph Siskovich, Joseph Snoy, John and Anne Spiller, Frank Taucher, Josephine Tratnik, Fred Vider, Josephine Zakrajsek, Jennie Zaman, Stanley Zele, Nace Zlemberger, and Jacob Zupancic.[51] Exceptionally prolific contributors were also Ivan Zorman, of a predominantly "neutral" or "middle range" ideological orientation, and Ivan Jontez, who started his writing career as a socialist, created some of his major works as a "neutral" novelist and poet, and in one of his novels moved to a conservative-rightist position.[52]

Finally, the lone representative of the extreme radical pole of the Slovenian American ideological continuum is Joseph Kalar (1906-1972), one of America's foremost revolutionary writers and poets, associate editor or contributing editor of *New Masses*, *Left Front*, *International Literature*, and *The Anvil*.[53]

This inevitably incomplete overview of Slovenian American literature—the literature of a numerically small and relatively unknown ethnic group—reveals a strong literary involvement in all areas of the ideological continuum, ranging from the religious literature by Bishop Baraga, currently an official candidate of the American Catholic Church for sainthood, to the radical literature of Joseph Kalar, a leading American revolutionary writer, poet, and editor. We suspect that a more detailed analysis of the Slovenian American literary works, excluding strictly religious literature, would show that the bulk of writings fall into the middle range, the "neutral" or moderate orientation, with continuing decrease as one moves to the more extreme positions on the far right or left.

Selected Characteristics of Slovenian American Literature and Literati

The Slovenian American *literati* have dealt with a considerable variety of themes. Kappus, Baraga, Franc Pirc, and several other missionaries created some of the early works on the American Indians. Adamic was a foremost writer on American ethnic groups—and on his native Slovenia and Yugoslavia. Klobuchar takes us to the little known American mountain ranges and hidden trails in search of beauty, courage, and a deeper humanity; and with Grdina and Kobal we visit Greece, Turkey, Israel, the Soviet Union, Bulgaria, Pakistan, India, Korea, Japan, and Formosa. With Baraga we can pray and meditate in the Indian, English, and Slovenian languages. Or we can immerse ourselves in theological writings by Smolnikar, Gruden, and Mihelic, each representing a completely different theological orientation. We can enjoy Vodušek's Slovenian poetry about St. Francis, Fortunat Zorman's religious writings in *Ave Maria*, and visit with Wolbang Slovenian missionaries in Zambia, on Madagascar, in Thailand, or in Japan.[54]

We can take nostalgic trips to Slovenia with almost all Slovenian immigrant writers and poets, including Franc Pirc, Kristan, Ivan Zorman, Adamic, Mauser, Valentin, Prisland, Rogelj, and Jakopič. With the humorist Terbovec we can laughingly visit the American West, walking occasionally in the seventeenth-century footsteps of Kappus. Or we can descend with Molek to the "graveyards of the living" where Slovenian and other miners were contributing their sweat, their health and, not infrequently, their lives for a better America. With Baraga we can plead for God's mercy and love; with Smolnikar, for a universal church, world government, and universal peace. After visiting vividly-portrayed scenes in mines and factories, in bars and hospitals, we can unite our voices with Kristan and Molek in advocating better working and living conditions for the working class. Milena Soukal takes us to the "Temples of Peru" in her sensitive search for brotherhood and love, while Kalar "prays" to thunder to put an end to exploitatation and oppression.

With Mauser we watch how John Kovach, abandoned and alone, dies next to his machine at the Cleveland Twist Drill Company in the heart of the Slovenian ethnic neighborhood which also inspired Mlakar's powerful Dostoevskian story. With Bukvich we analyze the uprootedness and alienation of the modern world. With Krasna we visit the "black villages" and with Katka Zupančič we revolt against man's inhumanity to man. With Smolnikar, Kristan, Adamic, Mauser, and Rausch we dream highly different dreams about a new humanity and a better world. Finally, we visit Jontez, who had traveled the whole continuum. Paralyzed by a stroke, he reads us his swan song. . . . "There is a time for everything. . . ." His face is pale. His voice trembles. We pretend to stare at the shelves filled with books, the poet's only possession. In America one is not supposed to cry! . . .

Yes, the themes differ. There is a tremendous variety. There is, as the *Cleveland Plain Dealer* of September 2, 1956, reported, "an unexplored field of literature." There are many voices of the many American ethnic groups. There are many voices within each ethnic group—a rich, unexplored field of literature.[55]

The occupations of the Slovenian American *literati* also represent a wide range. As far as we know, Adamic alone made his living as a writer. In harmony with the Slovenian literary tradition, a large proportion of Slovenian missionaries and priests, from obscure chaplains to famous bishops, were actively involved in literary pursuits. Many Slovenian American *literati* worked as editors and reporters on Slovenian ethnic newspapers, among them Kristan, James Debevec, Louis Pirc, Zaitz, and Molek, while others occupied editorial or reporting positions with American magazines and newspapers as, for instance, Klobuchar, Kocivar, Orehek, and Skerly.

The following examples suggest the wide variety of occupations held by the Slovenian American *literati*: Smrekar was a chaplain; Trunk, a pastor; Franc Pirc and Čebul, missionaries; Baraga and Rausch, bishops; Kalar, a lumberjack; Mauser (a former seminarian whose books are widely read in German, French, and Spanish translations) and Tomsic, factory workers; Mlakar was a coal miner, businessman, and reporter; Rogelj, an insurance representative; Grill and Robert Debevec, lawyers; Dr. Kern, physician; Stanley Zupan, a banking executive; Zorman, a composer and music teacher; Borstnik, a radio announcer; and Bren, Bukvich, Jerman, Kobal, John Modic, Nielsen, Prosen, and Surtz, university professors.[56]

The Slovenian immigrant *literati* failed to form a single, relatively permanent, unifying organization of their own, although many of them occupied leading positions in numerous Slovenian cultural, fraternal, educational, social, and other organizations. Those who were ideologically close to each other frequently gathered in small, informal circles or joined Slovenian language or university clubs, library clubs, and similar groups. The ideologically opposed or "incompatible" *literati* usually either ignored each other or competed for the souls of readers. However, there were notable exceptions, such as Vodušek, a Catholic priest and a sensitive poet, who was a friend and admirer of Kristan, a leading progressive and socialist writer; or Ivan Zorman, a moderate, "middle-range" poet and essayist, who cultivated friendship and cooperation with writers belonging to Catholic, neutral, progressive, and socialist camps. Several *literati* considerably changed their ideological orientations in the course of their writing careers, for

Dr. Frank Jauh Kern, physician, linguist and writer

instance, Louis Pirc, from progressive to Catholic-clericalist; Jontez, from socialist to neutral and, in one work, to conservative; Dr. Kern, from socialist to neutral; Adamic, from neutral to progressive and, some would say, leftist, etc.[57]

Slovenian American literature was published in both Americas, in several European countries, and in Australia, by a large number of Slovenian magazines, journals, almanacs, and newspapers. Several Slovenian American authors also appeared in American and international periodicals, including: *American Mercury, Family Digest, True,* and *Sports Afield* (Robert Debevec); *The Saturday Evening Post* (Adamic, Kobal); *Look* (Kocivar); *Time* and *Life* (Skerly); *Family Circle, Skyline,* and *Golf Digest* (John Modic); *Skyline* (S. Zupan, J. Modic); *Moreana, Philological Quarterly, Renaissance News,* etc. (Surtz); *Esquire, Common Ground,* etc. (Mlakar); *Journal of American Folklore, The American Slavic Review, The Slavonic Review,* etc. (Klancar); *New Masses, International Literature, Left Front, The Anvil,* etc. (Kalar); and *Harper's Magazine, The Living Age, The American Parade, American Mercury, New Republic, Reader's Digest, Saturday Review of Literature, American Scholar,* etc. (Adamic).[58]

Books by Slovenian American *literati* were published by a considerable number of Slovenian publishing establishments in the United States (Ameriška Jugoslovanska Tiskovna Družba, Ave Maria Press, Prosvetna Matica, Triglav, Equality Printers, etc.); Slovenia (Mohorjeva Družba, Slovenska Izseljenska Matica, Državna Založba Slovenije, etc.); Austria (Mohorjeva Družba v Celovcu); Italy (Mohorjeva Družba v Gorici); Argentina (Slovenska Kulturna Akcija, Baraga Editorial, Svobodna Slovenija); and elsewhere. Occasionally, Slovenian authors resorted to "samozaložba" (self publishing), where they served as their own publishers and distributors.

The Slovenian American literature written in English was issued by a large number of American and, occasionally, British publishers, ranging from Harper Brothers, Herder, and Vanguard Press to Yale, Princeton, Oxford, and the University of Chicago Press. Works by Slovenian American writers were also published by various houses in Austria, Germany, Switzerland, France, Spain, Sweden, and other countries by their respective native publishers.

While the bulk of Slovenian American literature was written in Slovenian, with works in English a close second, the Slovenian missionary *literati* were remarkably polyglot and often wrote with equal facility in Slovenian, English, German, French, Latin, and Indian languages. As a rule, other Slovenian *immigrant* writers were also fluent in many languages, especially in Slovenian, German, Italian, and English, while a few knew seven or more languages. Outstanding in this regard was Merkun, who studied and considerably mastered no fewer than twenty-seven languages.[59]

a : b = c : x, by Milan Vojsk

In general, it can be said that missionaries wrote in several languages in order to reach as many faithful as possible for religious proselytizing purposes and the immigrant writers other than missionaries usually wrote predominantly or exclusively in Slovenian to perpetuate the Slovenian language and heritage in America. The American-born *literati* of Slovenian descent wrote almost exclusively in English, although some of them (e.g., Mlakar) continued to show a preference for Slovenian themes, viewed often in the light of American rather than Slovenian values.

Among the substantial number of *literati* who wrote only in Slovenian are: Zaitz, Grdina, Kerže, Ambrožič, Rogelj, Vodušek, Jakopič, and Mauser. Others wrote only in English, for instance, Mlakar, Kocivar, Robert Debevec, and Kalar. Adamic, who came to America at fifteen, wrote a few minor pieces in Slovenian but all his major works are in English. Some *literati* wrote with equal facility in English and in Slovenian, among them Ivan Zorman, Klancar, Krasna, Jontez, Grill, Kern, Zaplotnik, and Prisland. Zakrajšek, whose main contributions are in Slovenian, also edited a religious magazine and wrote a number of minor works in Slovak. Kristan wrote mostly in Slovenian, but he also authored a book and several articles in German.

Counting works in original languages and translations, Slovenian American literature was published in at least the following languages: Slovenian, English, Otchipwe (Indian), Ottawa (Indian), German, Spanish, French, Latin, Swedish, Italian, Croatian, Serbian, Slovak, Czech, Greek, Arabic, Portugese, and Finnish.[60]

Impact and Contributions

It is still much too early to evaluate fully the impact and contributions of Slovenian American literature. We may, however, make a few tentative observations.

The Slovenian American *literati* have, undoubtedly, helped to preserve the Slovenian heritage in America and, to a lesser extent, among Slovenian minorities and immigrants in European and other countries. Their works have often had educational, recreational, and prestige value for their compatriots. Uprooted and destatused immigrants and their descendants took pride in private and public Slovenian libraries, containing various works authored by their Slovenian fellow-citizens. Translations from and into English and the appearance of works by Slovenian authors written originally in the English language have widened the circle of readers and stimulated cultural cross-fertilization, starting with Primec's translation of Benjamin Franklin from English to German and continuing up to the present time.[61]

The Slovenians have also made a considerable contribution to American Indian literature. Albert J. Nevins writes in *Our American Catholic Heritage* that "Bishop Baraga was the first of the American bishops to issue his pastoral letters in Indian."[62] Professors Cujes points out that a volume of over seven hundred pages of Baraga's meditations, *Katolik Enamiad*, first published in the Otchipwe language in 1850, was reprinted in 1939 as part of the Indian cultural revival, and that present-day missionararies and scholars are still using Baraga's Indian dictionaries and grammars. Similarly, writings by various Slovenian authors have made an important contribution to American Indian history, and the Indian songs, recorded by Baraga and several other Slovenian missionaries, have survived as examples of American Indian folklore and literature.[63]

In other areas, some contributions are still tentative, unknown, or invisible, and call for further research and documentation. Thus, for instance, Dr. John Modic, a Slovenian American, translated into English Johann Nestroy's play, *Einen Jux Will Er Sich Machen*. Thornton Wilder adapted this English translation for *The Merchant of Yonkers*, later rewritten as *The Matchmaker*, and finally resulting in the musical, *Hello, Dolly!*[64]

Other contributions which have become visible and even acclaimed have gone without mention of the Slovenian background of their creators, as, for example, Professor Bernard Jerman's *The Young Disraeli*, described by *Punch* of December 14, 1960, as "an absorbingly well-written book" and by the *Times Literary Supplement* of December 23, 1960, as "a work of genuine and exuberant scholarship." In 1971, American, British, French, and German scholars and writers jointly dedicated a "Festschrift," *Moreana—Meliora* to Professor Edward Surtz, an American writer and scholar of international reputation, the son of humble Slovenian immigrant parents from Cleveland, Ohio.[65]

Although the quality of Slovenian American literature is undoubtedly uneven, several Slovenian writers have had their works published in some of America's most prestigious periodicals, as we have already indicated. At least three Slovenian American writers (Adamic, Mlakar, and Kalar) were included in Edward J. O'Brien's *The Best Short Stories*. Adamic was frequently reprinted by *Reader's Digest*; one of his books was a Book-of-the-Month Club selection and was reprinted in a *Modern Classics* edition. He has also been included in Argentina's collection, *Obras Famosas* (Famous Works).[66] The works of Mauser, although practically unknown to American readers, have gone through a number of editions in German and Spanish translations. One of his books has been published in the prestigious French collection, *La pensée universelle* (Universal Thought), as "the work of a great Catholic author" and a second book has been selected for inclusion in the international collection, *Gigante*, as being among the "giants of world literature."[67] Frank Mlakar received awards for poetry and plays, but it was his novel, *He, the Father*, acclaimed by *Time* magazine as "a powerful Dostoevskian story,"[68] which gained him national recognition. Kalar was included not only in O'Brien's *The Best Short Stories*, but also in Conroy's *The Anvil Anthology*, as one of America's leading radical writers.[69]

Robert Debevec's story, "Long Shot to Kill," a factual account of the shooting of a Confederate general by a Union soldier, first published in *True Magazine*, was aired on national television in the General Electric True Series.[70] Similarly, Daniel Hrvatin's "Cleveland's Moon Shot" has brought him favorable national publicity,[71] and Jerome Turk has gained national and international recognition for such creations as "Concepts of Communication," "Listening in on Latin America," "The Many Faces of Mary," "Some Beloved Child," and the United States multimedia travel show seen at Expo '70 at Osaka, Japan.[72]

If it is true, as Gunnar Myrdal maintains, that the greatest American dilemma is a moral delimma—the dilemma of transforming the American Dream into reality,[73] then we may say that in this noble effort the Slovenian American writers have played a remarkable role. Bishop Baraga, in his fight for the preservation of Indian cultures, wrote books, grammars, and dictionaries in Indian languages a century before the American government adopted a more humane and pluralistic orientation toward these native Americans.[74] Professor Brewton Berry discusses Adamic as *the* leading exponent of cultural pluralism and cultural democracy in America,[75] a view, officially recognized by the United States Congress in 1972, which has become increasingly popular and powerful today.[76] Finally, Bishop Rausch put Adamic's America as a "Nation of Nations" into a world-wide universal context in his book, *A Family of Nations*, subtitled "An expanded view of patriotism—a new dedication to humanity."[77]

Epilogue

It has frequently been assumed that small and relatively unknown peoples or nations have contributed nothing, or very little, to the growth and progress of the cultures and civilizations of the world—and the same "logic" has often been applied to ethnic groups. Yet, the more we study relatively little-known peoples such as the Slovenians, the more we realize that size alone, among peoples as well as among individuals, has very little to do with productivity and creativity.

The Slovenians, for instance, were among the trailblazers of an ancient democracy that was admired by such men as Bodin and Jefferson. Baraga, an immigrant from Slovenia, was not only a giant of faith and an early authority on Indian languages, but one of the earliest American advocates of cultural pluralism. Dr. Frederic Pregl, the Slovenian-born, Nobel-prize-winning father of micro-analysis, revolutionized the fields of organic chemistry and medicine.[78] According to Dr. Von Braun's

The dawn of life, by H. Gregory Prusheck (Perušek)

History of Rocketry and Space Travel, Hermann Potočnik, who was forced to write under a German pseudonym, "Noordung," authored the first comprehensive scientific book on manned space travel and was also a pioneer in the field of solar energy.[79] An editorial in the *Atlanta Journal* of November 29, 1944, states that Max Stupar "has been called the father of mass airplane production" and also "contributed much to the development of the B-29 Superfortress" which helped America to win World War II.[80] Yet, who ever told Americans, or Slovenian American youth, that Stupar was an immigrant from Metlika, Slovenia?

America's pride at the New York World Fair in 1965 was a $250,000 car of the future. Who in the crowds of fascinated visitors suspected that this futuristic superstar of technology was designed and produced by John Bucik, an unassuming immigrant genius from Slovenia who also designs futuristic furniture, futuristic homes, and mini-submarines?[81] American newspapers wrote of President Ford's "first spectator outing as president at the Robert F. Kennedy Stadium in Washington"; yet, how many people in America knew that the stadium in question was designed by Alexander Papesh, a Slovenian American architect,[82] or that the nearby L'Enfant Plaza, described by the *Washington Post* as "a triumph of modern architecture," was designed by Araldo Cossutta (Košuta), an immigrant from Slovenia?[83] Cossutta, with L. M. Pei, a Chinese American architect, was winner of the 1968 Architectural Firm Award—the highest group honor conferred by the American Institute of Architects.

When President Nixon and his party went to China, they took along HP-35 pocket calculators "as the prime example of modern U.S. technology." These calculators were designed by Dr. France Rode, a Slovenian American,[84] but neither the Americans nor the Chinese had any idea that the object of their admiration was related to anyone or anything Slovenian. With not a single Slovenian contribution tc America or the world ever mentioned in their textbooks, it is no wonder that American students of Slovenian descent are often left with the impression that they belong to a very backward and sterile nationality group. What an injustice! What a pity! What a shame![85]

The ethnic literatures of America are only one of the many areas where ethnic contributions to our country have been neglected, ignored or belittled. The so-called ethnic revival has barely begun to scratch the surface. America is just beginning to unearth her many buried, unknown, or little-known treasures. As one of our writers, Katka Zupančič, put it, "the pot" —may we say "the melting pot"?—"is broken" and the treasures, great and small, which lay buried in it, must now be brought to light to enrich our multi-ethnic American heritage. A namesake of Katka, the Slovenian poet Oton Zupančič, invites us all to confront this great challenge of the third century of our history as an independent nation with these verses of universal appeal:

Forge me on thy anvil, Life!
Am I flint, then I shall flash.
Am I steel, then I shall sing.
Am I glass, then let me crash![86]

Let us hope and pray that America will never crash, that she will always flash as one of the great lights of freedom and justice—including justice to all her ethnic groups—and that, strong as steel, she will continue to sing in her many voices—this our Nation of Nations in the Family of Nations!

NOTES

1. Primož Kozak, *Slovenia* (Belgrade: Yugoslav Review, 1974), pp. 1-16, 81-112, 209-22. See also Milko Kos, *Zgodovina Slovencev* (Ljubljana: Slovenska Matica, 1955); Bogo Grafenauer, *Zgodovina slovenskega naroda*, I-V (Ljubljana, Zadružna Zveza, 1956-62); and John A. Arnez, *Slovenia in European Affairs* (New York: Studia Slovenica, 1958).
2. *Unknown Yugoslavia* (London: Herbert Jenkins, 1960), pp. 198-99.
3. R. G. A. De Bray, *Guide to the Slavonic Languages* (London: Dent and Sons, 1951), p. 365.
4. *The Native's Return* (New York and London: Harper and Brothers, 1934), p. 29.
5. *Tito's Imperial Communism* (Chapel Hill: University of North Carolina Press, 1947), pp. 10-11.
6. Adamic, pp. 29-31; Grafenauer, V, 179-204.
7. Joseph Felicijan, *The Genesis of the Contractual Theory and the Installation of the Dukes of Carinthia* (Celovec: Družba sv. Mohorja, 1967), p. 25.
8. Felicijan, pp. 53, 73-74, 81; and Kos, pp. 86-89. Facsimile of Bodin's text, initialed by Jefferson, appears in Felicijan, p. 15.
9. Felicijan, pp. 5, 9-10, 15.
10. Crane Brinton, rev. of *The Genesis of the Contractual Theory*, by Joseph Felicijan, *The Catholic Historical Review*, LIV, 4 (1969), pp. 657-58.
11. Helfried Patz, "Geschenke der Slowenen an die Welt," *Steirische Berichte*, IX, 5 (1965), p. 135.
12. *Hyperion* (Cambridge: The Riverside Press, 1893), pp. 360-72; Andreas Bernardus Smolnikar, *Denkwürdige Ereignisse im Leben des Andreas Bernardus Smolnikar* (Cambridge: Folsom, Wells and Thurston, 1838); *Proclamation of the True Union* (Donnely's Mill, Pa.: Perry Co., 1862); *The Great Encyclic Epistle* (Baltimore: S. S. Mills, 1865), etc. See also "Bernard Smolnikar" in Alfonz Gspan, ed., *Slovenski Biografski Leksikon*, X (Ljubljana: Slovenska Akademija Znanosti in Umetnosti, 1967), pp. 392-96.
13. "Marko Anton Kapus" in Izidor Cankar, ed., *Slovenski Biografski Leksikon*, III (Ljubljana: Zadružna Gospodarska Banka, 1928), pp. 426-27; and Erik Kovačič, "Pater Kapus—prvi slovenski misijonar v Severni Ameriki," *Ave Maria Koledar 1970* (Lemont: Slovenski Frančiškani, 1970), pp. 89-95.
14. Herbert E. Bolton, *Rim of Christendom* (New York: Russell and Russell, 1960), p. 464.

15. *Geschichte, Character, Sitten und Gebräuche der Nord-Amerikanischen Indier* (Ljubljana: J. Klemmens, 1837); *Abregé de l'histoire des Indiens de l'Amerique septentrionale* (Paris: La Societé de Bon Livres, 1837); and *Popis navad in zadržanja Indijanov polnočne Amerike* (Ljubljana: J. Klemmens, 1937).
16. Mila Šenk, "Štiri knjige Jožefa Grdine," *Slovenski Izseljenski Koledar 1968* (Ljubljana: Slovenska Izseljenska Matica, 1968), pp. 247-49; and "Jože Grdina 80-letnik," *Ameriška Domovina*, 3 March 1972, p. 2.
17. Andrej Kobal, *Svetovni popotnik pripoveduje* (Gorica: Mohorjeva Družba, 1975-76), 2 vols.
18. Klobuchar's books include: *The Zest (and Best) of Klobuchar* (1967), *The Playbacks of Klobuchar* (1969), *True Hearts and Purple Heads* (1970), *Will America Accept Love at Halftime?* (1972), *Where the Wind Blows Bittersweet* (1975). More detailed information can be found in *Slovenian Research Center of America Archives* (*SRCA Archives*: Willoughby Hills and Kent, Ohio). Each archive contains multiple data, such as *vitae*, bibliographies, clippings, copies, photographs, etc.
19. See footnote 4.
20. Henry A. Christian, *Louis Adamic: A Checklist* (Kent: Kent State University Press, 1971), p. xxvi.
21. Arnez, pp. 142-43; Ivan Prijatelj, *Kulturna in politična zgodovina Slovencev* (Ljubljana: Akademska Založba, 1838), 2 vols.; and Dr. Anton Kacin, "Dr. Anton Mahnič" in Dr. Rudolf Klinec, ed., *Zgodovina goriške nadškofije* (Gorica: Mohorjeva Družba, 1951), pp. 79-106.
22. Rudolph P. Cujes, *Ninidjanissidog Saiagiinagog: Contributions of the Slovenes to the Socio-Cultural Development of the Canadian Indians* (Antigonish: St. Francis Xavier University Press, 1968), pp. 58-92.
23. Fortunat Zorman, "Pokojni p. Kazimir," *Ave Maria Koledar 1959* (Lemont: Slovenski Frančiškani, 1959), pp. 128-31; and *SRCA Archives*.
24. Dr. Filip Žakelj, ed., *Duhovne misli škofa dr. Gregorija Rožmana* (Celovec: Družba sv. Mohorja, 1969); and *SRCA Archives*.
25. *Cerkvena poezija: psalmi, slavospevi in cerkvene himne* (Celovec: Družba sv. Mohorja, 1952); trans. Albin Škrinjar, *Jezus Kristus: Premišljevanja*, I (Trst: Samozaložba, 1962), II, 1963.
26. Joann Birsa, *Glory to God: A Collection of Slovenian Hymns in English Translation* (Denver: Holy Rosary Church, 1971); Valentin Spendov, O.F.M., *Organ Music in Slovenia* (Rome: Pontificio Istituto di Musica Sacra and Lemont: Ave Maria Press, 1973); and Alfred Fischinger, "Važen prispevek k cerkveni glasbi," *Amerikanski Slovenec*, 23 July 1975.
27. M.T., "P. Fortunat Zorman 60-letnik," *Ameriška Domovina*, 2 December 1974.
28. *SRCA Archives*.
29. Longfellow, pp. 360-72; John L. Zaplotnik, "Kako je Kamničan snoval komunski raj v Ameriki," *Ave Maria Koledar 1947* (Lemont: Slovenski Frančiškani, 1947), pp. 115-27; and Dr. Janez Stanonik, "Andrej Bernard Smolnikar," *Slovenski Izseljenski Koledar 1962* (Ljubljana: Slovenska Izseljenska Matica, 1962), pp. 170-74.
30. Gspan, p. 395.
31. *SRCA Archives*.
32. J. M. Trunk, *Amerika in Amerikanci* (Celovec: Samozaložba, 1912), pp. 544-605; Bernard Coleman and Verona LaBud, *Masinaigans: The Little Book* (St. Paul: North Central Publishing Co., 1972), pp. 281-303; P. Bazilij, "Viharnik je omahnil," *Misli*, November 1973, pp. 307-09; Germain Marc' Hadour, "Reverendo atque amando Patri Edwardo Surtz, S.J., amici Thomae Mori s.p.d.," *Moreana: Meliora*, 4 (1971), n.p.; and *SRCA Archives*.
33. Coleman and LaBud, p. 303. In addition to numerous articles and essays, Msgr. Zaplotnik authored two books: *De vicariis foraneis* (Washington:

The Catholic University of America, 1927); and *Janez Čebulj: misijonar v Ameriki* (Groblje: Misijonska Knjižnica, 1928). He also translated various literary works from English into Slovenian.

34. One of Valentin's works, on "rural scenes in Slovenia," appeared in Dr. Ferdinand Kolednik's French translation as *Le petit Tonček du Potok: Scenes de la vie rurale en Slovenie* (Montreal and Paris: Apostolat de Presse, 1961).

35. *The Family of Nations* (Huntington: Our Sunday Visitor, 1970); *Human Rights* (New Orleans: National Council for Catholic Laity, 1973); *The Right to Live* (St. Paul: College of St. Thomas, 1974); *Christian Values in Today's Society* (Cincinnati: Archidiocese of Cincinnati, 1975) and *Research in the Church* (Washington: Catholic University of America, 1975).

36. "Learning about America," *The Cleveland Press*, 5 May 1939; "Družina Ivana Zupana," *Novi Svet*. June (1941), pp. 167-68; "Pred 20 leti je umrl Jakob Debevec," *Ameriška Domovina*, 3 March 1972; "Zadnje slovo Johna Jericha," *Amerikanski Slovenec*, 17 October 1973; and *SRCA Archives*.

37. Zdravko Novak, "Slovenska zdomska knjižnica," *Ameriška Domovina*, 22 March 1971; Pavle Borštnik, "Pogreb pokojnega g. Zdravka Novaka," *Ameriška Domovina*, 8 December 1971; and *ARCA Archives*.

38. Dr. Tine Debeljak, "Panorama slovenskih leposlovnih ustvarjalcev v emigraciji," *Zbornik Svobodne Slovenije 1955* (Buenos Aires: Svobodna Slovenija, 1955), p. 231; Janez Sever, "Karel Mauser," a series of articles published in *Ameriška Domovina*, November 1952; "Karel Mauser petdesetletnik," *Glas Slovenske Kulturne Akcije*, 28 August 1968; and *SRCA Archives*.

39. "Library Board Fetes Mrs. Prisland," *The Sheboygan Press*, 24 September 1963; Debeljak, pp. 231, 234-36; and *SRCA Archives*.

40. Jože Bajec, "Biografije," *Slovenski Izseljenski Koledar 1967* (Ljubljana: Slovenska Izseljenska Matica, 1967), pp. 308-21; "Frank Kerže," in Izidor Cankar, ed., *Slovenski Biografski Leksikon*, III (Ljubljana: Zadružna Gospodarska Banka, 1928), p. 452; "Frank J. Kern," *Slovenski Biografski Leksikon*, III, p. 444; Theodore Andrica, "Slovenian Poet Reared in U.S. Gains Fame," *The Cleveland Press*, 24 September 1929; and *SRCA Archives*.

41. "Janko N. Rogelj," Gspan, p. 121; Bajec, pp. 316-17; Debeljak, p. 235; "Frank Mlakar," in William Coyle, ed., *Ohio Authors and Their Books* (Cleveland: The World Publishing Co., 1962), p. 450; John M. Urbancich, "Success Comes Easy to Bob Debevec," *The Euclid News Journal*, 16 March 1972; "Journal Editor Selected," *AAHS Newsletter*, May 1968; "Books of Interest," *The National Review*, 27 August 1960, p. 121; and *SRCA Archives*.

42. "Jože Ambrožič," *Čas*, 1923, p. 332; Debeljak, p. 236; Ludvik Potokar, *Zapiski* (Cleveland: Krog, 1951); Frank Česen, "Odlomek iz zgodovine St. Clair Avenije," *Slovenski Izseljenski Koledar 1970*, pp. 307-08; Louis Ule, "Cluster Analysis and the Authorship of Woodstock," *Revue* (Organization internationale pour l'étude des langues anciennes par ordinateur), No. 1 (1976), pp. 1-34; and *SRCA Archives*.

43. Christian, pp. i-xlvii, 1-142; "Louis Adamic," in Stanley J. Kunitz and Howard Haycraft, eds., *Twentieth Century Authors* (New York: The H. W. Wilson Co., 1942), pp. 4-5; and *SRCA Archives*.

44. Joža Mahnič, "Obdobje moderne," in Lino Legiša, ed., *Zgodovina slovenskega slovstva*, V (Ljubljana: Slovenska Matica, 1964), pp. 292-307; and Cvetko A. Kristan, "Etbin Kristan: borec za boljšo bodočnost delovnega ljudstva," *Prosveta*, 17 September 1970.

45. Frank Zaitz, "Jože Zavertnik: njegovo življenje in delo," *Ameriški Družinski Koledar 1930* (Chicago: Jugoslovanska Delavska Tiskovna Družba, 1930), pp. 149-61; Bajec, pp. 320-21; and *SRCA Archives*.

46. "Ivan Molek," in F. K. Lukman, ed., *Slovenski Biografski Leksikon*, V (Ljubljana: Zadružna Gospodarska Banka, 1933), p. 149; and Cvetko A. Kristan, "Ameriški slovenski književnik Ivan Molek," *Rodna Gruda*, September 1957, pp. 190-91.
47. Bajec, pp. 318-19; and *SRCA Archives*.
48. France Adamič, "France Magajna," *Naši Razgledi*, 5 November 1971, p. 643; and I. S., "France Magajna: kmet in pisatelj," *Rodna Gruda*, November 1971, p. 32.
49. Jože Bajec, "Bibliografija del Katke Zupančič," *Slovenski Koledar 1974* (Ljubljana: Slovenska Izseljenska Matica, 1974), pp. 318-25.
50. Jože Bajec, "Jubilej Ane Praček-Krasne," *Slovenski Izseljenski Koledar 1971*, pp. 206-07; and "Bibliografija Anne P. Krasne," *Slovenski Koledar 1975*, pp. 270-77.
51. Ivan Molek, "Petdesetletnica slovenskega časnikarstva v Ameriki," *Ameriški Družinski Koledar 1941*, pp. 28-36; Jože Bajec, "Petinsedemdeset let slovenskega časnikarstva v ZDA," *Slovenski Izseljenski Koledar 1967*, pp. 273-307; and *SRCA Archives*.
52. Correspondence by Ivan Zorman and Jontez, *SRCA Archives*.
53. Edward J. O'Brien, ed., *The Best Short Stories* (Boston: Houghton Mifflin Co., 1934), pp. 357, 362.
54. At the time of this writing, no library has a complete collection of all Slovenian American literary works. Among the best existing collections are those of the Slovenian National Library on St. Clair Avenue, Cleveland, Ohio; Slovenian Research Center's Collection, Willoughby Hills and Kent, Ohio; Franciscan Library, Lemont, Ill.; the SNPJ Collection, Burr Ridge, Ill.; the Library of Congress, Washington, D.C.; and the National and University Libraries, Ljubljana, Slovenia.
55. Illustrative of this situation is the fact that several Slovenian American authors appeared in prestigious French, German, Spanish, and other collections or series, while some American papers, which faithfully publicized ethnic card parties and foods, refused to mention the literary and other accomplishments of members of the same local ethnic groups, even when such accomplishments received national or international recognition. In this way, the image of ethnics as predominantly or exclusively blue-collar, lower-class people has been perpetuated.
56. In Slovenia, as well as among Slovenian Americans, it would be difficult to find a single occupation or profession whose members have not attempted to write prose or poetry. Students of literature and of sociology may eventually profit from a careful examination of these materials, both published and unpublished.
57. See footnote 21 and *SRCA Archives*.
58. Christian, pp. 1-66; and *SRCA Archives*.
59. Trunk, pp. 545-46, 553, 556, 565; Coleman and LaBud, pp. 282, 285, 287, 290; Edward Gobec, *Love Moves Mountains* (Bedford: The Home Press, 1960), p. 30; and Giles Edward Gobetz, "The Ethnic Ethics of Assimilation: Slovenian View," *Phylon: The Atlanta University Review of Race and Culture*, XXVII, 3 (Fall 1966), p. 271.
60. *SRCA Archives*.
61. In addition to this anthology and a collection of Slovenian American poetry, a detailed analysis of the role of the Slovenian ethnic writers, poets, dramatists, and translators, based on survey data, book reviews, and personal documents, will be published at a later date.
62. *Our Catholic Heritage* (Huntington: Our Sunday Visitor, 1972), p. 149.
63. Cujes, pp. 58-96; and *SRCA Archives*.
64. Correspondence and copies in *SRCA Archives*.
65. *Moreana: Meliora*, 4 (1971). See also "Fr. Edward L. Surtz Dies," *The Cleveland Press*, 20 January 1973.
66. Christian, pp. 70, 72.

67. Karel Mauser, *Kaplan Klemens*, trans. Bernhardt Strauss and Gerold Schmid (Luzern: Rex Verlag, 1955); *El capellan*, trans. José I. Belloch Zimmermann (Barcelona: Luis de Caralt, 1961), Col. *Gigante*: lo mas selecto de la literatura universal; *Yerné, le fils du défunt*, trans. Ferdinand Kolednik (Paris: La Pensée Universelle, 1974), etc.
68. "Books," rev. *Time*, 7 August 1950, p. 72. See also Coyle, p. 450; Joseph Zelle, "Slovenian Colony Here Is Background for Novel," *Cleveland News*, 19 July 1950; and Nelson Algren, rev. of *He, the Father*, *New York Times*, 30 July 1950, p. 12. The author gratefully acknowledges valuable information on Mlakar which has been supplied by Viola Mlakar, Helen Perusek, Rose Marie Prosen, and Edward Pekovnik, and will be more fully utilized in future publications.
69. "Collar," in Jack Conroy and Curt Johnson, eds., *Writers in Revolt: The Anvil Anthology* (Westport: Lawrence Hill and Co., 1973), pp. 91-96.
70. Urbancich, p. 5; and *SRCA Archives*.
71. Mark, "Cleveland's Moon Shot," *Variety*, 11 December 1963; and *SRCA Archives*.
72. Bob Seltzer, "Best Location Pays Off," *The Cleveland Press*, 12 July 1967; and *SRCA Archives*.
73. Gunnar Myrdal, *An American Dilemma* (New York: Harper and Row, 1944), pp. lxxi, 1-25.
74. Cujes, pp. 58-92; Nevins, p. 149; and Giles Edward Gobetz, Jože Goričar, and Peter Jambrek, "Yugoslav Sociology," in Raj P. Mohan and Don Martindale, eds., *Handbook of Contemporary Developments in World Sociology* (Westport and London: Greenwood Press, 1975), p. 281.
75. Brewton Berry, *Race Relations: Interaction of Ethnic and Racial Groups* (Boston: Houghton Mifflin Co., 1951), p. 13.
76. Hon. Richard Schweiker, "Implementation of Schweiker Ethnic Studies Bill," *Congressional Record*, Vol. 118, No. 155, 30 September 1972.
77. See footnote 35.
78. "Chemistry 1923: Presentation Speech by Professor O. Hammersten, Chairman of the Nobel Committee for Chemistry of the Royal Swedish Academy of Science," in *Nobel Lectures Including Presentation and Laureates' Biographies: Chemistry, 1922-1941* (Amsterdam, London, New York: Elsevier Publishing Company, 1966), p. 25; "Pregl, Fritz" in *Asimov's Biographical Encyclopedia of Science and Technology* (New York: Doubleday and Company, 1972), p. 801; and Milena Gobetz, "This Our Heritage: Frederic Pregl," *Zarja—The Dawn*, December 1976, pp. 25, 32.
79. Wernher Von Braun and Frederick I. Ordway III, *History of Rocketry and Space Travel* (New York: Thomas Y. Crowell Company, 1969), p. 202. See also, "Slovenec načrtoval vesoljsko postajo," *Tedenska Tribuna*, 29 December 1966; and "Pozabljeno dejanje stoletja?" *Večer*, 2 February 1972.
80. "A Sad Loss to Aviation," *The Atlanta Journal*, 29 November 1944. See also *SRCA Archives*.
81. "John Bucik: Prototype Auto Designer and Builder" (unpublished biography, 1975). See also Dan Jedlicka, "A Rolling Executive Suite," *Chicago Sun-Times*, 10 March 1974; "The Ex Has It All," *The Wingfoot Clan*, 3 October 1974; and *SRCA Archives*.
82. "Alexander A. Papesh" (unpublished biography, n.d.); Dino Ianni, "Cleveland Can Have a Domed Stadium Now," *WKYC Radio Editorial*, 26 January 1971; "Alexander A. Papesh," *The Cleveland Press*, 29 November 1971; and *SRCA Archives*.
83. Wolf Von Eckardt, "L'Enfant Plaza: A Triumph," *The Washington Post*, 16 November 1968. See also *SRCA Archives*.
84. "A Superstar is Born," *Measure*, June 1972, pp. 6-7; "Peninsula Firms Win Honors for New Products," *Palo Alto Times*, 20 September 1972; William L. Crowley and France Rode, "A Pocket-Sized Answer Machine

for Business and Finance," *Hewlett-Packard Journal*, May 1973, pp. 2-9; and *SRCA Archives*.

85. Several surveys suggest that American textbooks present a principally white, Protestant, Anglo-Saxon view of America's past and present and "there is not a single textbook which presents a reasonably complete and undistorted picture. . . ." See Committee on the Study of Teaching Materials in Intergroup Relations, *Intergroup Relations in Teaching Materials* (Washington, D.C.: American Council on Education, 1947); Lloyd Marcus, *The Treatment of Minorities in Secondary School Textbooks* (New York: Anti-Defamation League of B'nai B'rith, 1961); and Michael B. Kane, *Minorities in Textbooks* (Chicago: Quadrangle Books, 1970).

86. Oton Župančič, "Forge Me on Thy Anvil," in Janko Lavrin and Anton Slodnjak, eds., *The Parnassus of a Small Nation* (Ljubljana: Državna Založba Slovenije, 1965), p. 91.

Plowed fields, by Ted Kramolc

CONTRIBUTORS

Writers

LOUIS ADAMIC (1899-1951) was born in Blato, Slovenia, of Slovenian peasant parentage and, after completing two years of gymnasium in Ljubljana, came to America when he was "not quite 15." An American citizen since 1918, he visited every state in the Union and worked as a factory hand, miner, steel worker, and journalist, before developing an impressive career as writer, editor, and lecturer. In 1928, H. L. Mencken accepted his first article for The American Mercury, and his first book, Dynamite, was published in 1931. The Native's Return, published by Harper in 1934, transformed Adamic into a national celebrity—a status which was reinforced by numerous other books, including My America (1938), From Many Lands (1940), Two-Way Passage (1941), What's Your Name (1942), My Native Land (1943), and, especially, A Nation of Nations (1945). Adamic, who possessed the talents of a stimulating writer, social analyst, and critic, has been widely considered as the leading exponent of cultural pluralism in America. He served as general editor for "The Peoples of America Series," published by the J. B. Lippincott Company, which introduced him as "rising high above his lettered colleagues as the one to interpret with his brilliant, sensitive mind the infinite nuances in America's polyglot voice." Siding with Tito's Yugoslavia against rival Yugoslav groups and against Soviet pressures of the late 1940's, Adamic died in 1951 under mysterious circumstances. His death was officially declared as suicide, while careful researchers suggest he was assassinated for political reasons.

DR. FRANK BUKVICH (BUKVIČ) was born in Slovenia and spent a considerable part of the Second World War in Hungarian concentration camps. After having received his doctorate in political science from Graz University, Austria, he worked and studied in the United States and was awarded a doctorate in modern languages by New York University. A naturalized American citizen and current chairman of the Department of Slavic *and Germanic Languages at Fairfield University, Dr. Bukvich has authored numerous short stories, essays, and novelettes and is best known for his psychologically penetrating novels,* Brezdomci *(The Homeless, 1948) and* Ljudje iz Olšnice *(The People from Olšnica, 1973). A member of several American and Slovenian professional organizations, Professor Bukvich is also an associate of The Slovenian American Institute—The Slovenian Research Center of America, Inc.*

JIM DEBEVEC was born in 1938 in Cleveland, Ohio, of Slovenian immigrant parents and attended St. Joseph High School and John Carroll University. Like his father James and his brother Robert, Jim has shown an early interest and talent in writing. In 1971 he joined the Collinwood newspaper chain as a free-lance writer and in 1972 he began writing a weekly column in the Euclid News Journal. *An author of numerous feature articles and short stories as well as an enthusiastic photographer, Jim has recently served as editor of the* Richmond Heights Journal *and of the Slovenian daily newspaper,* Ameriška Domovina.

DANIELA DOLENC, a native of Slovenia and now a naturalized Canadian citizen, was put into a concentration camp by the Nazis at the age of thirteen, while a high school student in Maribor, Slovenia. "Survivors," published in this anthology, is the true story of her experiences as a young girl in the Gestapo prison. She came to Canada with three children in 1958 to join her husband, Ivan Dolenc. Active in dramatics, she has also been a contributor to the Canadian Veterans Review *and the Slovenian American daily newspaper,* Prosveta. *She is employed as a receptionist at the Toronto University Clinic.*

IVAN DOLENC, like his wife Daniela, experienced the horrors of the Nazi occupation of Slovenia until freed by the American army in 1945. After the war, he studied Slavic languages and literatures and comparative world literature at the University of Ljubljana, Slovenia, and then became a professional journalist, writing a cultural column for the Maribor daily Večer *and serving as an editor of the weekly magazine* 7 dni *and of the publishing house* Obzorja. *He has edited numerous volumes of children's books and novels and also translated novels from English and German into Slovenian. He came to Canada in 1956, worked at many manual jobs, and received his Master of Arts degree from the University of Toronto. He now teaches modern languages and English literature in North York. His articles and short stories have been published in a number of ethnic newspapers (*Prosveta, Glas Naroda, Ameriška Domovina, *and others) as well as in such "old country" magazines as*

Dialogi *and* Rodna Gruda. *Since 1976 he has also been publisher and editor of the* Slovene Canadian Diary-Dnevnik.

IVAN JONTEZ worked in Slovenia as a farm laborer and came to America in 1929. Since his early youth, he has been in love with Slovenian literature and has also familiarized himself with the leading American, English, German, and Russian authors. Having worked in a number of factories and offices, as well as a salesman, journalist, and editor, Jontez has never tired of observing and analyzing human behavior and of reading and writing. He gained reputation as a novelist with such books as Senca preko pota *(A Shadow across My Path, 1940),* Jutro brez sonca *(Morning without Sun, 1949), and* Trouble on East Green Street *(1956). He is also a poet and the author of numerous short stories, essays, and dramatizations and writes with equal facility in both Slovenian and English. In the 1940's, he succeeded Etbin Kristan as editor of* Cankarjev Glasnik—*in all probability the best Slovenian American literary magazine.*

FRANK KERŽE (1876-1961) belonged to the literary club "Sloga" (Harmony) as a student in Slovenia and was influenced by such leading Slovenian literati *as Ivan Cankar, Josip Murn Aleksandrov, and Dragotin Kette. Thirsting, as he said, for broader horizons, he came to American in 1904 and worked as a journalist with* Glas Naroda, Glasilo SNPJ, *and* Prosveta. *He also edited* Komar *(The Mosquito, 1905-07), the first Slovenian humorist paper in America,* Naš Gospodar *(Our Economist, 1912-14), and* Čas *(Time, 1915-28), a leading Slovenian American literary and educational monthly magazine. Most of Kerže's poems, short stories, novelettes, and novels were published, often serially, in various Slovenian American periodicals, especially in* Čas. *He was particularly strong as an educational writer and essayist. He was also very active in Slovenian cultural, economic, and political affairs. His son, Frank Kerže, Jr., has been employed in various executive positions with the U.S. Atomic Energy Commission.*

TED KRAMOLC was born in 1922 at St. Vid near Ljubljana, Slovenia, as the son of Professor Luka Kramolc, a noted collector and arranger of Slovenian folk songs, and of Maria Kramolc, a teacher. While a student of architecture at the University of Ljubljana, he also studied painting and drawing in the studios of such leading Slovenian artists as Matej Sternen, Božidar Jakac, and France Gorše. After his immigration to Canada in 1948, he worked as a railroad section hand. He graduated with honors from Ontario College of Art and now lives with his family in Toronto, Canada. His short stories were published in Jutro, Naša Volja, Koroška Kronika, *and* Koroški Fužinar *in Slovenia and in such ethnic publications as*

Meddobje *and* Zbornik Svobodne Slovenije *in Argentina, and* Ameriška Domovina *in the United States. A bilingual writer and poet, Kramolc is also and primarily a painter. He has exhibited in Canada, Europe, and South America, as well as in the United States. His works are to be found in numerous prestigious collections, including the Government of Slovenia Palace, Art Gallery of Sarnia, Art Gallery of Ontario, National Gallery of Canada, and Douglas Duncan Collection. He is listed in several leading reference works, including* Who's Who in American Art *and* International Directory of Arts.

ANNA KRASNA hails from Vipavsko, Slovenia, and came to America in 1920, where she lived first in small Pennsylvania mining towns, then in Chicago, and, for some three decades, in New York. She started writing poems while a grade-school pupil in Slovenia and soon became known among Slovenian Americans for her poems, short stories, essays, and articles which were published in Prosveta, Proletarec, Mladinski List, Ameriški Družinski Koledar, Cankarjev Glasnik, Enakopravnost, *and* Glas Naroda. *Her collection of poems,* Za lepše dni *(For a Better Future, 1950), is of literary as well as of sociological interest. Always active in Slovenian and American cultural and educational affairs, Mrs. Krasna worked as a journalist and was editor of* Glas Naroda, *a New York-based Slovenian newspaper published daily and, later, three times a week. She and her sick husband, Adolph, returned to Slovenia in 1972. Now a widow, Mrs. Krasna continues to write a column for* Prosveta, *a Chicago-based Slovenian daily newspaper.*

ETBIN KRISTAN (1867-1953) developed a considerable reputation as a socialist writer, poet, and labor-movement organizer in Slovenia and Austria before his immigration to America in 1912. In the New World, he soon became the leading Slovenian socialist writer, poet, and dramatist who influenced a generation of literary and political followers. He served as Yugoslav Immigration Commissioner in New York until 1927 and was editor of several socialist or progressive publications, including Ameriški Družinski Koledar, Proletarec, *and* Cankarjev Glasnik. *He published several collections of poems, short stories, and novels, and over a dozen powerful dramas, in Slovenian, and a book of short stories and essays,* Skizzen *(Sketches, Vienna, 1902), in German. He was also a prolific speaker and organizer who visited over seven hundred Slovenian communities throughout the United States. Often characterized as the greatest Slovenian New Dealer before the New Deal, Kristan died in Slovenia at the age of 87. His widow, Mrs. Frances Kristan, lives in Michigan and is a member of The Slovenian American Institute—The Slovenian Research Center of America, Inc.*

KAREL MAUSER (1918-1977), who came to America in 1950, has generally been considered the most influential contemporary Slovenian American Catholic writer. A former seminarian, he supported his family as a worker at the Cleveland Twist Drill Company while writing at night and on weekends. He wrote over twenty highly popular novels, many of them based on peasant life in Slovenia, several dramatizations, and a large number of short stories. His trilogy, Ljudje pod bičem *(Men under the Whip, 1963-66), which describes the suffering of Slovenians during the Nazi-Fascist occupation and communist revolution of the Second World War, has often been considered his* magnum opus. *His* Chaplain Clemens, *first published in Slovenian (*Kaplan Klemen, *1965), appeared in German and Spanish translations, the latter in the collection* Gigante, *among the "giants of world literature." One of his books was also published in Dr. Ferdinand Kolednik's French translation as* Yerné, le fils du défunt *(Paris: La Pensée Universelle, 1974). Mauser's short stories, poems, and occasional ideological-political articles and essays were published in a number of Slovenian ethnic publications, including* Amerikanski Slovenec, Ave Maria, *and* Ameriška Domovina *in the United States,* Božja Beseda *in Canada,* Meddobje *and* Zbornik Svobodne Slovenije *in Argentina,* Koroška Kronika *and* Naša Luč *in Austria, and* Misli *in Australia.*

FRANK MLAKAR (1913-1967) was born of Slovenian immigrant parents in Cleveland, Ohio, and won his first literary prizes as a student at the Collinwood High School where he was active in dramatics and poetry. At the height of the Depression he moved to New York and after a number of jobs became the secretary of Louis Adamic, who encouraged him to write. Later he became assistant editor of Common Ground, *published and edited by Louis Adamic. In addition to poems, dramas, and short stories, Mlakar wrote a novel,* He, the Father *(Harper, 1950), which received nationwide publicity and was described as a "powerful, Dostoevskian story" by* Time *magazine. In 1942, he married an Australian schoolteacher and in 1953 moved to Australia to manage her family's retail business. The couple had two daughters, the older of whom, known as Christina Malakar, became Victorian and Australian National Junior Champion and was cited in the Melbourne* Sun *of November 9, 1967, as "the fastest junior in Australia." Frank Mlakar died in Australia from stroke at the age of 54, just after completion of his drama, "Francie," on which he had worked the last eighteen months of his life.*

JOHN MODIC, a second-generation Slovenian American born in Cleveland, Ohio, is a professor of English literature and linguistics at Indiana-Purdue University at Fort Wayne, Indiana. Dr. Modic's short stories, poetry, articles, and trans-

lations have appeared in journals as widely different as Comparative Literature *and* Kiwanis Magazine. *He has also contributed to the new* Encyclopedia of World Literature in the Twentieth Century, Ball State Forum, Windless Orchard, Family Circle, Skyline, *and to other periodicals. He has written and lectured on Gascoigne, Ariosto, James Joyce, Thornton Wilder, Thomas Wolfe, Stanley Elkin, C. P. Snow, Ivan Lah, and Louis Adamic. Past president of the American Federation of Teachers at his university, he is also very active in various professional organizations.*

*IVAN MOLEK (1882-1962) was born in Slovenia and came to America at the age of eighteen. He worked as a foundry laborer and miner and since 1905 as journalist and editor of a number of Slovenian papers (*Glasnik, Glas Svobode, Proletarec, *and* Prosveta*). Socialist in orientation, he was a prolific writer of short stories, dramatic works, essays, and articles as well as a translator and, with less success, poet. His most impressive books are* Dva svetova *(Two Worlds, 1932),* Veliko mravljišče *(The Huge Anthill, 1934), and* Sesuti stolp *(The Tower That Collapsed, 1935). Upton Sinclair's* Jimmie Higgins *is his best-known translation into Slovenian (1921). His widow, Mrs. Mary Jug-Molek, has recently published a comprehensive annotated bibliography of his works, with English translation of the titles and a valuable introduction.*

JOHN P. NIELSEN was born the son of the Slovenian immigrant family Šešek in Cleveland, Ohio, in 1911. He obtained his Ph.D. from Yale University in 1947 and after experiencing employment discrimination against his Slovenian surname, he reluctantly changed it to Nielsen. Taking with him an unending interest in his Slovenian roots, Dr. Nielsen moved to New York where he served as professor of metallurgy and department chairman at New York University for twenty-nine years. He is now professor emeritus at Polytechnic Institute of New York and professor of dental materials science at the Dental School of New York University. Founder of the International Precious Metals Institute, Dr. Nielsen is also past president of the Metal Science Club of New York and of Alpha Sigma Mu, the National Metallurgical Honorary Society. Originator of the Shell-Nielsen shear test for porcelain-metal interfaces and an inventor with a number of patents on gold alloys, he has published several new theories on the behavior of metals on annealing and was for nineteen years editor of Metallurgy/Education Yearbook. *As president of the Sniffen Court Association, he was responsible for attaining national landmark status for Sniffen Court, a small exclusive community in the heart of New York where he owned a house. Dr. Nielsen, who was selected head of the first delegation of American technical men to visit the Soviet Union, reads several languages, including Slovenian, and has published in American and Slovenian periodicals a number of short stories and articles on his travels, his ethnic background, and his personal experiences. A recipient of numerous scientific and civic awards and honors, Dr. Nielsen is also a trustee of The Slovenian American Institute—The Slovenian Research Center of America, Inc.*

ZDRAVKO NOVAK (1909-1971) was born in Slovenia where he was active in various Catholic-oriented organizations prior to his immigration to America in 1949. A leading member of the post-World War II political immigrants and a historian of the communist revolution in Slovenia and of the recent Slovenian political immigration in America, Novak authored over two hundred short stories and articles, three dramatizations, and two major books, Pota božja *(God's Ways, 1957) and* Utrinki *(Fragments, 1959). He established an impressive collection of publications authored or published by the "new immigrants" of Slovenian descent, which he willed to the Slovenian College,* Slovenicum, *in Rome, Italy. Many of his literary and historical contributions were published in* Tabor, Zbornik Svobodne Slovenije, Ameriška Domovina, Amerikanski Slovenec, *and other Slovenian ethnic publications. While in America, he was also active in "Tabor," "Lilija," the Slovenian School at St. Mary's Parish in Collinwood, and in other religious and cultural Slovenian ethnic organizations in Cleveland, Ohio. "A Patch of Earth" expresses his longing for his native land at a time when he was already incurably sick from cancer.*

MARIE PRISLAND arrived in America in 1906 as a young girl and started working at six cents an hour while attending evening classes after work. Too poor to become a schoolteacher, she developed a remarkable career as a leader and teacher of Slovenian American women. In 1926 she became the founder and then served for over twenty years as president of the Slovenian Women's Union of America; in 1929 she initiated Zarja-The Dawn *magazine for which in 1977 she still writes an interesting monthly column in English and Slovenian. She has written hundreds of articles for* Zarja, Amerikanski Slovenec, *and other magazines and papers, including the* Wisconsin Magazine of History; *edited* Woman's Glory—the Kitchen *(1963); has written the history of the Slovenian Women's Union; and authored a book of recollections,* From Slovenia to America *(1968). Active in numerous Slovenian and American civic, educational, charitable, and cultural affairs, Mrs. Prisland has received several honors and awards, including the Order of St. Sava from the Yugoslav government in 1938, and in 1946 an American Red Cross Citation signed by President Truman. Now in her eighties and very active in scholarship drives for American Slovenian and Carinthian Slovenian minority students, Mrs. Prisland is also a trustee and senior associate of The Slovenian American Institute—The Slovenian Research Center of America, Inc.*

ROSE MARY PROSEN was born of Slovenian immigrant parents in Cleveland, Ohio, where she is currently professor of English at Cuyahoga Community College. Her poems have been published in Poetry Venture, California Quarterly, Free Lance, Carroll Quarterly, College English, Epos, Everyman, Green Apple, New Review, Italian-Americana, Spirit, Tangent, *and* The Little Review *as well as in* Poetry: Cleveland *(1971),* Four Poets *(1974), and* Cleveland Anthology *(1975). She also has to her credit two independent collections,* Poems *(1971) and* O the Ravages *(1977). She won third prize in the Cleveland State University Poetry Forum Competition, and her reminiscences, "Looking Back," reprinted by permission in this anthology, took first place in Dr. Michael Novak's "Growing Up Slavic in America EMPAC Competition." Ms. Prosen has also authored articles in* College English *and the* Illinois Schools Journal.

JANKO ROGELJ (1895-1974) came to America in 1913, studied at Dubuque College in Iowa, and settled as an insurance representative in Cleveland, Ohio, where he became active in Slovenian fraternal and cultural organizations. He was the first editor of Enakopravnost *(Equality, 1918) and for many years president of the Slovenian National Home and of the Slovenian National Library on St. Clair Avenue in Cleveland. He wrote numerous historical, literary, and educational articles, a history of the Slovenian National Home on St. Clair, and three collections of short stories and poems:* Kruh in srce *(My Bread and My Heart, 1962),* Skrivnostni klic *(A Mysterious Call, 1967), and* Svoji k svojim *(For Our People's Sake, 1973). A longtime close friend and collaborator of the late Louis Adamic, Rogelj was also an active associate of The Slovenian American Institute—The Slovenian Research Center of America, Inc. He spent the last years of retirement in his native village of Primskovo, near Kranj, in Slovenia where he died in 1974 while working on a book of* memoirs.

SISTER LAVOSLAVA TURK was born in Celje and completed Teachers College in Ljubljana, Slovenia. She arrived in America in 1921 and taught a generation of Slovenian American children in various Slovenian ethnic parochial schools in Kansas and Wisconsin. After a loss of hearing forced her out of the classroom, she began writing for various Slovenian American magazines and newspapers, especially for Ave Maria, Ameriška Domovina, *and* Amerikanski Slovenec. *Her first book,* Pesem šolske sestre *(The Song of a School Sister) was published in 1974, and two additional books are expected on the market in the near future. As a senior associate of The Slovenian*

American Institute—The Slovenian Research Center of America, Inc., Sister M. Lavoslava Turk has also collected many valuable historical materials on Slovenians in America. Now in her eighties, she remains very active as writer, columnist, and a SRCA research associate.

KAZIMIR ZAKRAJŠEK, O.F.M. (1878-1958) came to America in 1906 and became editor of several Slovenian American Catholic periodicals: Sloga *(Harmony),* Edinost *(Unity),* Glasnik Presvetega Srca Jezusovega *(The Sacred Heart of Jesus Messenger),* Ave Maria *magazine, and* Ave Maria Koledar *(Ave Maria Almanac). He also edited* Sveta Rodina *(Holy Family) and* Listy sv. Františka *(St. Francis Messenger) in Slovak and* St. Francis Magazine *in English. A member and officer of the Gallery of Living Catholic Authors, Father Zakrajšek also authored numerous books, among them:* Abecednik za ameriške Slovence *(Guidelines for American Slovenians, 1917),* Pri kapelici *(At the Chapel, 1918),* Spominska knjiga župnije sv. Štefana *(Souvenir Book of St. Stephen's Parish, 1923),* Molitvenik za ameriške Slovence *(Prayer Book for American Slovenians, 1925); dramas,* Prisegam *(I Swear, 1932),* Za srečo v nesrečo *(Unhappy Search for Happiness, 1932); and a book of* memoirs, Ko smo šli skozi morje bridkosti *(As We Went through a Sea of Sorrows, 1941). A towering figure among Slovenian Catholics in America, Father Zakrajšek was also the founder of the Holy Cross Commissariat of Franciscan Fathers (1912), and of the Franciscan Monastery and of Mary—Help of Christians Shrine (1923) at Lemont, Illinois, a leading Slovenian pilgrimage in America.*

STANLEY ZUPAN, son of the Slovenian American immigrant poet Ivan Zupan, served as editor of Glasilo KSKJ, *of* Marquette News, *and of* Skyline, *the literary quarterly of Cleveland College. He retired in 1976 from his thirty-year banking career as manager and assistant vice president of St. Clair Savings in Cleveland, Ohio. An award-winning writer of short stories and author of many articles and essays, Zupan is additionally a past president of the Wickliffe Rotary Club and a member of the Wickliffe Civil Service Commission, the Wickliffe Citizens Advisory Council, the Wickliffe Chamber of Commerce, and the St. Clair Business Association. A graduate of Western Reserve University and the Cleveland Advertising Club School, and well-known for his leadership in Slovenian and American cultural and civic affairs, Zupan has also served as a trustee of The Slovenian American Institute—The Slovenian Research Center of America, Inc.*

KATKA ZUPANČIČ (1889-1967), together with Anna Krasna, is considered the leading Slovenian American progressive woman writer and poet. She was born in Bela Krajina, Slovenia, graduated from Teachers College in Gorica, and served for ten years as a teacher in her native land before emigrating to America in 1923. A partial bibliography of her works compiled by Joseph Bajec of Ljubljana shows 305 poems, five dramas, 137 short stories and articles, and seven translations. Her best-known work, Slike iz vsakdanjega življenja *(Impressions from Everyday Life), was published by Prosvetna Matica of Chicago in 1946. Katka wrote for a large number of Slovenian American magazines, almanacs, and newspapers and was a leading contributor to* Mladinski List *(The Voice of Youth). She was married to Jacob Zupan, also an immigrant from Slovenia, a writer, and a post office executive who contributed many ideas for the improvement of postal services, including the original idea and design for the extension "snorkels" on mailboxes which now allow America's motorists to deposit letters without leaving their cars. Katka and her husband were active in numerous Slovenian fraternal, cultural, and educational organizations.*

Artists*

LILLIAN BRULC, born of Slovenian immigrant parents in Joliet, Illinois, is a painter, printmaker, and sculptor. She holds Master of Fine Arts degrees from both the School of the Art Institute of Chicago and the University of Chicago and has also studied in Europe under a foreign travel fellowship. She has done major works in architectural environments, including murals and sculptures at the Archdiocesan Latin American Committee in Chicago and at the Panama Mission in San Miguelito, Panama. Her paintings and prints have been exhibited at the Art Institute of Chicago and at several galleries, colleges, and seminaries. She has taught at a number of colleges, the School of the Art Institute of Chicago, and the Divine Word Seminary at Techny, Illinois, and is currently on the faculty of the Chicago Academy of Fine Arts. A member of many professional organizations as well as of the Art and Exhibits Committee of The Slovenian American Institute—The Slovenian Research Center of America, Inc., Miss Brulc has recently completed a series of drawings and illustrations for book publication and is presently working on new figure sculptures.

NANCY BUKOVNIK is the granddaughter of Toné Kmet, who was immortalized by Louis Adamic as "The Old Alien by the Kitchen Window," and the daughter of Antoinette, nee Kmet, and the late John Bukovnik, a popular Slovenian immigrant photogra-

*With the exception of Božidar Jakac, who lives in Slovenia but spent some time in America, and of Lillian Brulc, Nancy Bukovnik, Steven Rebeck, and John Kapel, who were born in America of Slovenian parentage, all artists represented in this volume are Slovenian immigrants who created a large portion of their art works in America, Canada, or Australia. The biographical sketch of Ted Kramolc appears among the writers.

pher. She graduated with honors from Monticello College in Godfrey, Illinois, where she was art editor of the Monticello Times *and from the Cleveland Institute of Art where she was one of the finalists for the Gund Award. A self-employed artist commissioned by individuals as well as by major American corporations throughout the nation, she has illustrated numerous publications, ranging from the* Campus Personal Directory *for Ohio Bell to children's books and school texts. She has done commercial art, is particularly fond of fairy tales and animals, and has also created beautiful landscapes and portraits. Miss Bukovnik has received numerous prizes and awards, including the Gold Medal Award from the Cleveland Society of Communicating Arts, CA Magazine Award of Excellence, and an Award of Distinction for outstanding achievement in the field of graphic communications presented at the Chicago 1 Exhibit in 1961. She lives in Gates Mills, Ohio, and is a member of the Art and Exhibits Committee of The Slovenian American Institute—The Slovenian Research Center of America, Inc.*

FRANCE GORŠE was born in 1897 in Zahomec, Slovenia. He studied art at Zagreb Academy of Fine Arts under the famous sculptor, Ivan Mestrovic. He opened his own studio and art school in Ljubljana in the early 1930's and taught art in Trst (Trieste) between 1945 and 1952. Arriving in Cleveland, Ohio, in 1952, he became an American citizen in 1957. Gorše spent eighteen very creative years in Cleveland and New York where he organized an art school and the Slovenian art club, "Lok," before returning to Europe to open his own art gallery at Sveče in Slovenian Carinthia, Austria. His powerful art has been exhibited and acclaimed in many countries, including Yugoslavia, Austria, Italy, Denmark, Argentina, Canada, and the United States. His sculptures are preserved in churches in all parts of America (notably in the National Shrine of Immaculate Conception in Washington, D.C.), Canada, and Europe as well as in American and European museums, art galleries, and private collections. Considered one of the great contemporary sculptors and painters, he was the subject of a special monograph, Sculptor France Gorše, *compiled by John Arnez and Rudy Vecerin and published in 1971 by Studia Slovenica, and of a film produced by Anthony Zrnec of Toronto, Canada, in 1976. Gorše, now in his early eighties, is still active—and ceaselessly innovative—executing major orders in Slovenia, Austria, Canada, and the United States.*

BOŽIDAR JAKAC was born in 1899 in Novo Mesto, Slovenia, studied at the Academy of Arts in Prague, Czechoslovakia, and has become known as one of Slovenia's leading graphic artists. He is the only artist represented in this Anthology *who is neither an immigrant nor a descendant of Slovenian immigrants. He has, however, repeatedly toured America and other countries and portrayed so many Slovenian immigrants in America (some of whom appear as authors in this book) and elsewhere that he must be acknowledged an ethnic painter par excellence. Jakac has been awarded numerous prizes and honors in his native Slovenia and Yugoslavia as well as in America (including two awards from the Cleveland Museum of Art), in France, and in Switzerland. He is one of the representatives of the world-famous Slovenian school of graphic artists whose reputation has made Ljubljana, Slovenia, a permanent host of the International Exhbitions of Graphic Art.*

JOHN A. KAPEL was born in 1922 in Cleveland, Ohio, the son of Slovenian immigrant parents, Ivan and Ivanka Kapel, both of whom have been very active in Slovenian fraternal, cultural, and educational affairs. A graduate of Ohio Wesleyan University, he studied art at the Yugoslav Art School in Cleveland under the direction of H. Gregory Prusheck (Perušek), at Prague University in Czechoslovakia, and at Cranbrook Academy of Art in Bloomfield Hills, Michigan. The Second World War found him in the Navy at Pearl Harbor, then in Guam and Germany. After employment with Halle's and Swedish Modern, Inc., he went to California in 1954 where he has become widely known as one of America's leading independent industrial designers. He continues to be active also in other forms of art, including painting and sculpturing. John has four sisters and a brother who, like their parents, are very active in Slovenian ethnic affairs, particularly the Slovene National Benefit Society, the SNPJ Recreation Farm, Jadran and Circle No. 3 singing societies, and The Slovenian American Institute—The Slovenian Research Center of America, Inc. John's wife, Priscilla Todd-Kapel, is a well-known American sculptress in her own right. Related to President Lincoln's wife, she comes from a leading American family but enjoys preparing favorite Slovenian foods and has learned to speak Slovenian fluently.

H. GREGORY PRUSHECK (PERUŠEK) was born at Jelovec, near Sodražica, in Slovenia in 1887 and came to America in 1906. As a young man, he travelled so widely throughout the United States and Mexico that he was nicknamed by many American sources the "vagabond artist" who enjoyed presenting exhibitions "for the masses." After the First World War he settled in Chicago, Illinois, and in 1931 he moved to Cleveland, Ohio, where he established the Yugoslav Art School and served as its director until 1940. Undaunted by periods of extreme poverty, Prusheck was an exceptionally resourceful and creative artist whose art underwent gradual transformation from naturalism to abstract symbolism and expressionism. He exhibited widely throughout America as well as in France and Yugoslavia and won numerous awards, including the Jenkins Prize and the Carr Prize. He is listed in several prestigious reference sources, among them

Art of Today *(1932),* Who's Who in American Art *(1940), and* Dictionnaire critique et documentaire des peintres, sculpteurs, dessinateurs et graveurs *(Critical and Documentary Dictionary of Painters, Sculptors, Designers, and Engravers, 1954). Prusheck, who was frequently described by American critics as "the best of the modernistic painters of Chicago" in the 1920's, died in Cleveland, Ohio, in 1940. His daughter, Mrs. Marian Brandon, inherited her father's talent for painting and is a member of the Art and Exhibits Committee of The Slovenian American Institute—The Slovenian Research Center of America, Inc.*

STANISLAUS RAPOTEC was born in 1911 of Slovenian parents in Trst (Trieste), grew up in Ljubljana, Slovenia, and studied economics and the history of art at the University of Zagreb in Croatia, Yugoslavia. Put in charge of secret Allied missions in Yugoslavia and the Middle East during the Second World War, Rapotec later studied art in Vienna and other cities and migrated to Australia in 1948. "He paints as he has lived: richly, strongly, without hesitancy," writes Australian art critic William Olson in the Sidney Daily Mirror *of March 3, 1961. Rapotec has exhibited in several Australian art galleries and museums and has become nationally known as one of the best abstract painters of Australia. Described as "a big man, 6 foot 2, but too gentle to kill a rat which invaded his studio," Rapotec won the Blake Prize, one of Australia's most coveted awards, in 1961, for his* Meditating on Good Friday, *an entirely non-figurative painting. He is listed in a number of prestigious sources, including* The Modern Encyclopedia of Australia and New Zealand *(1964). An article about Rapotec which describes him as being "of immense significance for the development of art in Australia" was translated in 1971 from English into Slovenian by his Slovenian immigrant friend, Misha (or in Slovenian Miša) Lajovic, who in 1975 became the first immigrant and the first non-Anglo Saxon politician in the history of Australia to be elected to its Senate.*

STEVEN A. REBECK was born in 1891 in Cleveland, Ohio, the son of Slovenian immigrant parents and was in 1912 the first sculptor to graduate from the old Cleveland School of Art. Up to his mid-eighties, he has earned a livelihood creating portrait plaques of famous politicians, actors, industrialists, and other notables as well as sculpturing statuary, cupids, gargoyles, and medals. His portrait plaques include President John F. Kennedy, Dr. Martin Luther King, Ernie Pyle, the famed war correspondent, and the composer of musical comedies, Cole Porter. His sculptures include a bust of Shakespeare in the Cleveland Cultural Garden, the War Memorial in Alliance, Ohio, the stations of the cross and other religious works in several Catholic churches, and a sphinx twelve feet high and twenty feet long sculptured for the Masonic Temple of St. Louis,

Missouri. As you daily see Mack trucks on the highway, you may recall that the bulldog symbols for the Mack Trucks Corporation were made by Rebeck and that the executive vice president of this giant firm is Frank Pryatel, also the son of Slovenian immigrants. Rebeck has won numerous awards, including a first prize at a Cleveland Museum of Arts May Show, and is listed in a number of leading American and European reference works on art.

STANKO TUSEK was born in Hrastnik, Slovenia, in 1939 and migrated with his parents to Melbourne, Australia, in 1950. One year later, he won third place in a state-wide poster competition among schools. In 1957 he received the Senior Year University High School Art Award and also served as art editor of his school magazine. During the same year, he also won first place in the under-18 section of the Sun Youth Art Show so highly praised by both Australian Premier Bolte and the Minister of Education, Mr. Bloomfield, as reported in the Melbourne daily Sun *of August 30, 1957 (graciously sent to the senior editor of this* Anthology *by Rev. Basil Valentin). Tusek graduated from Melbourne Teacher's College and in 1966 received his Diploma of Fine Art in Sculpture at the Royal Melbourne Institute of Technology. He served as head of art departments in various Australian high schools and participated in several exhibits, including a travelling exhibition of the National Gallery and Council of Adult Education and Print Council of Australia Exhibition in 1967 and the Twenty-Four Point Plug Show at the Argus Gallery in Melbourne, and a Print Council of Australia Exhibit at the University of Tasmania in 1968. In 1970 Tusek moved to Toronto, Canada, where he was appointed head of the Art Department at Runnymede Collegiate Institute.*

MILAN VOJSK was born in 1922 in Beltinci, Slovenia, and studied sculpture at the Academy of Art in Munich, Germany, where he was awarded second prize in a student competition, and at the Academy of Fine Arts in Ljubljana, Slovenia, from which he graduated in 1947. He sculptured several monuments, portraits, and figural compositions in Maribor, Slovenia, prior to his emigration to Sydney, Australia, in 1957. His works of sculpture are represented in the National Art Gallery in Maribor and the National Museum in Ljubljana, Slovenia; the National Museum in Belgrade, Yugoslavia; the National Art Gallery—Adelaide in Australia; the Reserve Bank of Australia; and in numerous other public and private collections. He has created murals for some of the leading hotels in Sydney and for Kensington University and was commissioned for a number of "city" sculptures, including a Fountain with Sculpture (a ten-foot sitting nude) erected in the Legal Precinct, London Circuit, in Canberra, the capital of Australia. First brought to the attention of the senior editor of this Anthology *by D. S. Lajovic, the Slovenian immigrant president of Impact International Pty., Ltd., and the recipient of the Australian Export Award in 1967, Vojsk is listed in several prestigious works, including* Australian Encyclopedia Yearbook *(1965) and Longman's* Religious Art of Australia *(1967).*

Translators

JOSEPH F. KESS is presently an associate professor of linguistics at the University of Victoria, British Columbia, Canada. He was born of Slovenian immigrant parents in Cleveland, Ohio, in 1942 and received his Bachelor of Science degree cum laude *from Georgetown University in Washington, D.C., and his M.A. and Ph.D. degrees from the University of Hawaii in Honolulu. He has studied in the Philippines, Japan and Yugoslavia and has carried out research on a variety of language structures. He was lecturer in Tagalog at the University of Hawaii and language coordinator for the Peace Corps Philippine Project at Hilo, Hawaii. A recipient of several honors, awards, and fellowships, Dr. Kess authored over twenty scholarly articles and a college textbook,* Psycholinguistics: Introductory Perspectives *(Academic Press, 1976). His parents, active in Slovenian ethnic affairs, conscientiously helped him master both Slovenian and English in his preschool years. Today Professor Kess knows, in addition to these, Spanish, French, Croatian, Russian, Latin, Japanese, Haida, and Tagalog. A loyal American who is at the same time deeply interested in his Slovenian heritage, Dr. Kess is a member of the Editorial and Education Committees of The Slovenian American Institute—The Slovenian Research Center of America, Inc.*

EDWARD KRASOVICH was born in Eaton, Colorado, a farming community where his Slovenian immigrant parents worked on a beet-tending contract. After completing his college studies, he taught Latin, English, and Spanish for five years, worked for the traffic department of the Colorado Milling and Elevator Company fourteen years, and was an officer, including supreme secretary and editor, of the Western Slavonic Association for sixteen years. Since 1971 he has been in the motel business in Wyoming where he was elected secretary-treasurer of the Wyoming Motel Association in 1972. A man of quiet leadership, integrity, and hard work, he has held numerous other offices, including that of president of the Cody Kiwanis Club, deputy grand knight of the Knights of Columbus Council, and president of the Wyoming Catholic Laymen's Retreat Association. A past editor of Fraternal Voice *and a columnist of* Colorado *weekly, Krasovich has also translated Slovenian poems and prose into English and has served for many years as a hard-working volunteer research associate and a member of the Editorial Committee of The Slovenian American Institute—The Slovenian Research Center of America, Inc.*

MARY MOLEK was born of Slovenian immigrant parents, Frank and Lucy Jug, in Chicopee, Kansas; graduated from Kansas State College in Pittsburg, Kansas; and taught high school before moving to Chicago where she met Ivan Molek, whom she married in 1934. Subsequently she took graduate work at the University of Chicago, earning an M.A. degree and being admitted to Ph.D. candidacy in 1944. Her career includes positions of school psychologist, school social worker, counselor, college instructor, adult education teacher, and archives' curator. Throughout her twenty-eight year marriage, she worked closely with her husband in translating and writing and in participating in his fraternal and political activities. Her own articles and translations have been published in several Slovenian American progressive periodicals, including Mladinski List—The Voice of Youth. *Since Ivan Molek's death in 1962, she has translated his autobiography,* Čez hribe in doline *(Over Hill and Dale) and his semi-autobiographical work,* Dva svetova *(Two Worlds) and in 1977 published his comprehensive bibliography and a novel about an immigrant woman.*

RICK SUSTARIC (or in Slovenian Bogomir Šuštarič) was born in Predgrad, Slovenia, in 1934, came to America with his parents, and graduated from Grover Cleveland High School in Ridgewood, Long Island, New York. During the Second World War he served with the famous Tenth Mountain Division and was awarded the Conspicuous Service Cross, the Silver Star, Purple Heart, and other decorations. After military service, he graduated from Cornell University, earned his M.A. degree from the University of Pennsylvania in Philadelphia, and pursued his education toward the Ph.D. at the University of California, Berkeley. A teacher of social studies, he was particularly interested in American Indians, Blacks, Orientals, and Slavs and wrote a series of articles on ethnicity, slavery, and other topics. He was particularly fond of the Slovenian writer Ivan Cankar (1876-1918) and repeatedly visited his birthplace at Vrhnika, Slovenia. He translated Etbin Kristan's "The Invisible Bridge" while in the hospital already seriously ill—his last contribution to literature and to The Slovenian American Institute—The Slovenian Research Center of America, Inc., in which he was active since the early 1960's. He died at the age of 43, shortly before the publication of this Anthology.

FLORENCE F. UNETICH was born of Slovenian immigrant parents in Cleveland, Ohio. After high school, she worked as a secretary before enrolling at Ohio State University in 1962. Elected to Phi Beta Kappa and Chi Delta Phi English honorary, she graduated summa cum laude *with a B.S. in education and a B.A. in English. After completing her Master's degree in 1972, she has been teaching American literature and advanced placement English in Collinwood High School in Cleveland, Ohio, and freshman English at Lakeland Community College. Active in the Slovenian community since childhood, she attended Slovenian School and was a member of the Slovenian Junior Chorus. She has been a mainstay of Jadran Singing Society of which she is president. An accomplished soprano, she has performed in numerous concerts and musical productions in Ohio, Pennsylvania, Michigan, and Yugoslavia and has been widely acclaimed for her solo and ensemble work. She is featured with Angela Zabjek and Gil Dobida on a popular "Jadran Trio" record and has served as officer and member of the Editorial Committee of The Slovenian American Institute—The Slovenian Research Center of America, Inc. She also edited the* Adamic Symposium Program Book, *published by the Progressive Slovene Women of America in 1977.*

JOSEPH A. VALENCIC, born of Slovenian immigrant parents in Cleveland, Ohio, in 1954, has been active in Cleveland area Slovenian affairs since the age of six when he joined the SNPJ Junior Chorus, Circle No. 2. At the age of eleven, he was a member of the Lake Erie Opera Theatre and appeared in the Britten opera, Albert Herring, *with the Cleveland Symphony Orchestra at Severance Hall. He attended high school in Cleveland and at Phillips Academy in Andover, Massachusetts. He is presently a graduate student in graphic art and art history at Kent State University where he has been active as a singer with the New Kent Singers, cartoonist for the* Daily Kent Stater, *assistant slide librarian for the Art History Department, editor of* Human Issue, *and tutor in Slovenian. He has illustrated two textbooks and participated in university student exhibits. In 1975 he was awarded the Slovenian Studies Award, presented jointly by Kent State University and The Slovenian American Institute—The Slovenian Research Center of America, Inc.*

JOSEPH ZELLE, the son of Slovenian immigrant parents, holds a B.A. degree from John Carroll University (1939) and a Master's degree in English from Western Reserve University (1942). A native Clevelander, he was employed as a radio technician with the Columbia Broadcasting System and the Office of War Information in New York, and, after the Second World War, as consultant radio engineer, technical writer, technician, and chief engineer with leading radio stations in Cleveland, Ohio. He has also been an instructor of physics at Cuyahoga Community College and John Carroll University and of Slovenian at Cleveland State University. Fluent in several languages, he has been a contributor of articles and short stories to a large number of Slovenian and American periodicals and has been active in many Slovenian and American organizations, including his own Slovenia Film, the Catholic Mission Aid Society, and The Slovenian American Institute—The Slovenian Research Center of America, Inc. He has translated a number of works from Slovenian into English, produced a documentary film on the life and works of Bishop Frederic Baraga, and has received several honors and awards, including a Public Service Commendation, Edison Radio Amateur Award, and Consistent Reporting Award. Zelle attracted nationwide attention in 1957 as the first American to tune in Sputnik and to broadcast its signals on the radio station WERE.